The Mitchell Beazley
Nature Library
Trees

Keith Rushforth

BOOK CLUB ASSOCIATES
LONDON

Nomenclature

Popular names of trees vary widely; this makes them unreliable, and accuracy is best served by employing the scientific (Latin) name, the structure of which is governed by strict international rules. All trees have a double name: the first element is that of the genus, and the second the name of the species within the genus. For example, the birches are known as the *Betula* genus, and the Silver birch is the *pendula* species, and so the Silver birch is known as *Betula pendula*. Genera with noticeable similarities are grouped into families, and *Betula* belongs in the Betulaceae.

Sometimes further definition is required beyond the species. A variety (indicated by "var." after the specific name) is a tree that has developed slightly different characteristics from its species (or "type") due to regional ecological factors. A cultivar (cv.) or clone is propagated vegetatively from a cutting from a tree that showed some minor genetic change. It is given a new name, which is printed in inverted commas. A hybrid (denoted by "x" between the generic and specific names) is a natural cross between two species. Where the parentage of a hybrid is in doubt, as with many *Prunus* hybrids, a popular name replaces the specific name.

Acknowledgements

The author and publishers would like to thank the following people and organizations for their help: **Alf Westall and Malcolm Scott,** Bedgebury National Pinetum, Kent; **Alan Mitchell,** The Forestry Commission, Alice Holt Lodge, Farnham, Surrey; **Jim Keesing and Charles Erskine,** The Royal Botanic Gardens, Kew; **Ivan Hicks,** West Dean Estates, Chichester, Sussex.

Artwork
Jacket: **John Davis**
Olivia Beasley: 22/23, 28/29, 32/49, 52/59; **John Davis:** 73/83, 130/145; **John Michael Davis:** 21, 26/27, 30/31, 50/51, 60/69, 116/129, 146/167; **Annabel Milne and Peter Stebbing:** 5/8, 11/20, 24/25, 70/72, 168/188; **David Moore:** 1, 84/97, 106/115; **Paul Wrigley:** 98/105

Contents

Introduction

This book is a field guide that will enable the reader to identify almost any tree he or she encounters. Although Great Britain boasts only some 35 native species, many other introduced species are familiar. In this book we have been able to illustrate over 350 species as well as mention other species, varieties and cultivars. This means that all commonly encountered trees, with the exception of those rarely found outside arboreta, should be readily identifiable.

There is a generally accepted order in which tree families should be placed, based upon their presumed evolutionary sequence from the more primitive to the advanced groups. Occasionally I have deviated from this in order to place side by side species which bear a strong resemblance to each other so that they may be more readily identified. Within families the genera have been ordered purely for the sake of convenience, and their sequence does not imply any botanical significance.

A tree is usually defined as a woody perennial plant growing on a single stem to a height of 6 m or more, whereas a shrub does not attain this height and has a stem divided near the ground. But of course plants do not fall obligingly into these man-made categories all the time, and some of them occur as either a tree or a shrub. The rule I have followed is that if a plant occurs as a tree with more than a negligible frequency, then it should be included. Two plants included on these grounds, but often excluded from tree books, are Juniper and Ivy. I have also tried to pay particular attention to the appearance of deciduous trees in winter, a phase of their existence all too often ignored in books.

Points about size can only be made in general terms; this particularly concerns the bole, which increases in diameter every year—a distinctive characteristic of the growth of trees. The girth of the trunk 1.5 m above the ground is a reasonable method of estimating the age of a tree, and the rate of growth shows a remarkable degree of consistency amongst the species. The average increase in girth of a tree growing in the open is 2.5 cm a year; thus, if it has a girth of about 2.5 m, it is about 100 years old. The celebrated yew slows down after 100 years, and with a girth of 10 m could be up to 1,000 years old. All measurements given in this book are maxima.

How to use this book

The annotated illustrations, text and symbols, which are explained below, give in concise form all the information necessary to identify a tree, but you do not need laboriously to thumb your way through the book looking for the right species. The first step is to read the introductory pages, where the major differences between groups of trees are explained, and guidance is given on which parts of the tree to examine to narrow the choice. Once in the field you can use the three keys to identify the genus; from there you can proceed quickly to the species in question. Before you try to identify an unknown tree it is a good idea to practise using the keys by working backwards from one that is familiar.

More general matter will be found in the introduction to the broadleaf trees, p70.

Symbols

Symbol	Meaning	Symbol	Meaning
®	Rare, usually found only in collections		Needles in fascicles of 5
	Deciduous, i.e. leaves shed in autumn		Leaves in horizontal sprays along shoot
	Evergreen, leaves retained into winter		Found in deciduous woods
	Buds and leaves alternate or spiral		Found in evergreen woods
	Buds and leaves in opposite pairs		Found in mixed woods
	Leaves awl- or scale-like		Common in streets, parks and gardens
	Leaves in rosettes on short (spur) shoots		Found in open countryside
	Needles in fascicles of 2		Found by water or on wet or moist sites
	Needles in fascicles of 3	♂ male	♀ female

Abbreviations

alt	alternate	lf	leaf	sim	similar
br	branch	lflt	leaflet	sp(p)	species (plural)
c.	about	lvs	leaves		
cm	centimetre	m	metre	uns	underside
cv	cultivar	mm	millimetre	ups	upperside
fl	flower	opp	opposite	var	variety
fr	fruit	sev	several ·	vn	vein
infl	inflorescence	sh	shoot	yr	year

How to identify trees

The identification of trees is a matter of putting together all the various pieces of information provided by the plant, and not just some of them. It is very tempting to latch on to some immediately striking feature and go no further, in which case you might well end up wrongly identifying a tree, as your only piece of evidence was misleading. For instance, you might know that ashes are generally characterized by pinnate leaves, and so never entertain the possibility that the tree in front of you with single leaves is an ash—but there is an exception to the rule, the Single-leaved ash. So whenever possible examine the foliage, buds, flowers, fruit, habit and bark, or as many as are visible at that time of the year.

The first step, before using the keys in this book, is to decide whether a tree belongs to the conifers or the broadleaf trees, something almost anybody can do. The actual difference is that the conifers have exposed ovules (which develop into seeds) whereas the broadleaf trees bear theirs enclosed in an ovary, but for identification purposes the differences indicated by the colloquial names of the groups are sufficient: the conifers bear cones, and have needle-like leaves which contrast with the wider foliage of the broadleaf trees.

Besides observing as many features as possible, bear in mind a few general points. Even within the plant, leaf character varies, the leaves at the top generally being smaller (although poplars are a notable exception). The number of lobes usually decreases with age, and a fine example of this is Holly. Remember that shoots of a tree that has been pruned will grow with abnormal vigour, giving rise to untypical proportions. As a rule you will find more typical features on short shoots. Features which generally occur in pairs can be found in threes or even fours, for example sycamore fruits and the buds of Raywood ash.

Foliage characteristics

Foliage should be examined thoroughly. First, important observations can be made at some distance from the tree itself, such as the colour of the foliage, and whether or not it is pendent (hanging). With more detailed examination, leaves provide clues in variation of outline, and the way they are set upon the shoot. Other features to look at are the margins, the shape of the base and tip, the veins and the petiole, and the texture and hairiness.

Conifers: the illustrations below show four types of leaf arrangement. **Fascicles** (**a**), borne by pines, are bunches of needles growing from one bud (needle is not a scientific term but simply a descriptive alternative to leaf). Leaves set in a **pectinate row** (**b**), such as those of the yews and firs, are arranged in ranks along opposite sides of the shoot. **Awl-shaped leaves** (**c**), as borne by the junipers, are set radially around the shoot. **Scale-like leaves** (**d**), set densely round the shoot, are characteristic of Lawson cypress. See also the introduction to conifers, p19.

a   b   c   d

Broadleaf trees: the illustrations below show some basic leaf shapes of broadleaf trees, which have more varied foliage than the conifers. An important point to remember is that these are mostly deciduous, and are found in their mature form for a relatively short time.

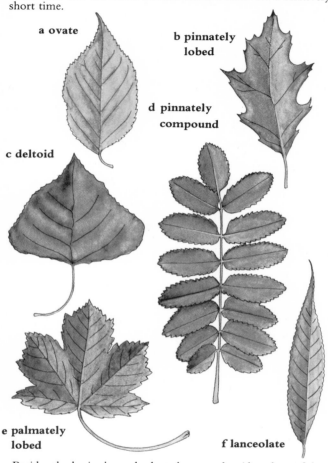

a ovate

b pinnately lobed

d pinnately compound

c deltoid

e palmately lobed

f lanceolate

Besides the basic shape, look at the **margins** (the edges of the leaf), which are serrated in **d** and **e** and entire in **b**; the **apex** (the end of the leaf farthest from the shoot), which is acute (or pointed) in **c** and acuminate (or needle-like) in **a**; and the **base** of the leaf, which is rounded in **a**, cuneate (or wedge-shaped) in **b** and **f**, truncate (or squared) in **c** and cordate (or heart-shaped) in **e**. See also the introduction to broadleaf trees, p 70.

a   b   c

The **petiole** or leaf stalk (above) can provide useful clues when its shape, particularly in cross-section, is examined. It is usually round **a** but can also be grooved **b**, as in Wild cherry, or flattened **c**, as in Aspen. There is a bud at the base of the petiole, and usually the petiole is curved around it in a crescent shape. In some species, however, the bud is completely enclosed in the enlarged petiole base during the growing season; when the leaf falls, it leaves a scar which encircles the bud.

Shoots and buds

Shoots are the new growth that springs from the buds at the start of the new season. They usually harden into their mature wooden state by midsummer and are then ready to bear the buds for the next season's growth.

Points to look for on shoots are the colour, whether they are hairy or not, and their shape. Most shoots, when seen in cross-section, are round, but they can be angled or winged in some species. Cutting across a shoot reveals its basic structure, which is shown in illustration **c** below. In the centre there is always the **pith**, sometimes a useful identification guide; it is generally a soft amorphous mass of various colours and textures, but is occasionally chambered, as in **b**.

The **buds**, borne through the winter before producing the new growth, are a key identification feature. There is usually a single bud on the end of the shoot, known as the terminal bud, from which the shoot will continue to grow. Lateral buds are arranged along the sides of the shoot, and produce new lateral shoots or leaves. The way in which these lateral shoots are arranged can vary considerably, and the main differences are illustrated above. They can be set alternately as in **a**, **b** and **d**, or in opposite pairs as in **c**.

Buds are a useful identification guide where they are set in different ways; a few trees, such as the cypresses, do not have a terminal bud in winter, while oaks are distinctive through having a cluster of buds at the shoot tips. Many trees have buds laid down and covered by the bark; they remain dormant until the main shoot is damaged or more light reaches the bole, when they start growing and produce what are called epicormic shoots.

Other features to look for in buds are such obvious points as the shape, size and colour, all of which differ widely. Buds may be ovoid, round, conic, cylindrical or spindle-shaped. Some species may have resinous or sticky buds **c**. One other key feature is the number of scales on the outside of each bud: some may be naked and have no scales at all, or they may have one **d**, two **b** or many scales **a** and **c**, usually adpressed on top of each other.

Thorns

Thorns are characteristic of a few species and occasional in others. The first and most obvious difference is the number in which they occur: the illustrations above show typical formations of thorns which grow in ones **a**, twos **b** or threes **c**. They are usually derived from shoots, and often carry buds at the base **a**.

Bark

The bark, the protective outer covering of the stem, can be a useful identification feature, especially as it is available throughout the year. Although the young branches have smooth bark, that on the bole is usually split and broken as the diameter of the stem increases with age. It is the form that this breaking up takes which can be diagnostic, and the chief characteristics, such as colour, are usually more pronounced in the bark higher up in the tree than in the mature bark near the base, because it has broken up more recently. Three basic types of bark are shown in the illustrations below: scaly fissures **a**, peeling bark **b** and ridged and furrowed bark **c**. The fissure colour can be important.

a   b   c

Glossary

Adpressed Closely pressed to an adjoining part of the plant, such as a bud against a twig or shoot (Hornbeam p93)

Alternate Leaves arranged singly along and on both sides of a stem

Aril Fleshy outer covering of a seed (Yew p22)

Auricles Ear-like appendages at the base of a leaf (Pedunculate oak p99)

Awl-like leaves Leaves tapering to a slender, sharp point

Axil Upper angle formed between a twig and a shoot, or the junction between two veins

Axil tufts Pubescence in axil

Bipinnate Advanced type of pinnate leaf whose leaflets are themselves pinnate (Honey locust p146)

Blade Greatest part of a leaf, the part other than the leaf stalk

Bloom Powdery or waxy sheen of a shoot or leaf (Eucalyptus p74) which can easily be rubbed away

Bole Trunk or stem of a tree

Bract Modified leaf associated with a flower. In some trees they are more conspicuous than the flowers themselves (Dove tree p173); in conifers bract scales often extend beyond the edge of the fertile scales (p19)

Buttress Strengthened part of a bole or root that assists in supporting a tree (Beech p94)

Calyx Green cup of sepals, outside the petals, supporting the flower

Carpel Single unit of a flower comprising the stigma, style and ovary

Catkin Dense, usually long and pendent, group of flower bracts

Chambered pith Pith of a shoot that is broken up by hollow spaces

Ciliate Leaves having a hairy fringe to their margins

Columnar-conic Shape of a habit which is narrow and straight sided at its base and then becomes pyramidal

Compound Leaves comprising several separate leaflets

Coppicing The practice of cutting back trees such as willows to their stumps in order to promote growth

Cordate Heart-shaped; used especially of leaves (Mulberry p113) where the leaf bases curve away from the leaf stalk

Corymb Domed or flat-topped flower cluster with the external flowers opening first (p71)

Crenate Serration which has broad, rounded teeth

Crown Upper part of the tree; the branches and foliage

Cultivar Variety of tree selected in cultivation

Cuneate Wedge-shaped base of a leaf tapering into leaf stalk (Cork oak p102)

Cupule Circle of bracts which become cup-shaped and enclose fruit such as an acorn

Cyme Flat-topped flower cluster, the central flowers opening first

Dioecious Having male and female flowers on separate trees

Drupe Fruit containing a seed in the form of a stone

Entire Margin without either teeth or lobules

Exserted Extended beyond the surrounding component

Fascicle Bundle or cluster (p6)

Fastigiate Tree habit which has very upswept, almost erect branches (Lombardy poplar p75, Cypress oak p99)

Fluted With alternate ridges and grooves (Dawn redwood p38)

Glabrous Smooth, not hairy

Glaucous Covered with a blue-grey or whitish bloom

Globose Irregularly spherical

Habit General appearance of a tree, usually from a distance

Hilum Paler, basal seed scar of a nut (Yellow buckeye p167)

Hybrid Species arising from the cross fertilization of two members of the same genus in which case the generic and specific names are separated by an 'x' (*Tilia* x *euchlora*) or (far less commonly) the members of two genera when the 'x' may precede the generic name (x *Cupressocyparis leylandii*)

Illobulate Entire, not bearing lobes

Imbricate Overlapping like roof tiles

Impressed vein Vein set below surface of leaf (Hornbeam p93)

Inflorescence Floral part of a plant

Involucre Circle of bracts developed to cover a fruit (Beech p94)

Lanceolate Shaped like the blade of a spear, as most willow leaves (Crack willow p80)

Layering The ability of a tree to regenerate by a branch touching the ground where it roots and forms a new plant

Leader Leading shoot of tree and so one of the youngest; may droop and thereby be an identification feature

Leaf scar Imprint left on a twig or shoot of a fallen leaf. Also known as "leaf trace"

Lenticel Raised corky growth on twig or shoot which admits air to the interior of the branch

Lobe Rounded section of a leaf, divided by sinuses

Lobulate Bearing small lobes

Margin Leaf edge

Midrib Central vein of a leaf

Monoecious Having both male and female flowers on the same tree

Oblique Unequal sided base of a leaf, as in most elms (p107)

Obovate Ovate with the widest part beyond the middle of the leaf

Obovoid Ovoid and largest beyond the middle

Operculum Cap of fused petals that covers flower bud of Eucalyptus (p174), falls as flower opens

Opposite Set in pairs at the same level each side of the twig or shoot

Orbicular Almost circular shaped leaf

Ovate Leaf that is egg-shaped in outline, widest below the middle (p6)

Ovule Part of the plant that becomes the seed after fertilization

Palmate Leaf that has lobes or leaflets radiating from one simple point, like the fingers of a hand (p6)

Panicle Compound inflorescence whose flowers branch from a central stem

Pectinate 2-ranked arrangement of leaves either side of a central shoot in the nature of the teeth of a comb

Peduncle Flower stalk

Peltate Shield-shaped

Perfect Having male and female organs combined in one flower and not as separate flowers

Petiole Leaf stalk

Petiolule The stalk attaching leaflets to a central rachis

Pinna Leaflet or primary division of a pinnate leaf

Pinnate Compound leaf with leaflets arranged regularly each side of a rachis (p6)

Pith Softer, central section of a shoot's stem

Pneumataphores Special aerial root of Swamp cypress (p37) that provides air to roots on waterlogged sites

Pollarding The practice of lopping trees at about 3 m above the ground in order to encourage further growth

Pome Fruit of several carpels enclosed in thick flesh (Crab apple p130)

Pubescence Covering of soft and short hairs

Pulvinus Swelling on some conifer shoots from which each leaf grows (p40)

Raceme Inflorescence of stalked flowers growing from a rachis

Rachis Central stalk of a compound (pinnate) leaf or inflorescence

Samara Winged fruit (Sycamore p155)

Serrate Toothed

Sessile Non-stalked

Sheath Tubular envelope enclosing a bunch of fascicle leaves (Pine p40)

Simple Leaf consisting of one single blade (Tulip tree p119)

Sinuate Strongly waved

Sinus Recess between lobes

Stipule Appendage usually at the base of a petiole

Stomata Orifices in a leaf used to let air into the leaf

Sub-sessile With a minute stalk

Ternate Set in threes

Tomentose Having a dense, woolly pubescence

Trifoliate Leaf comprising 3 leaflets

Truncate Abrupt end to a leaf base or tip

Umbel Inflorescence with pedicels all arising from the same point (p71)

Umbo Raised centre of the scale of a pine cone

Valve Section into which a fruit capsule splits

Venation Pattern of veins

Vein axils Upper angle between two veins

Identification keys

Don't shy away from botanical keys; they are a tried and tested aid to tree identification. The keys to conifers, broadleaf trees and leafless winter shoots included here will lead you to the genus of the tree concerned; from the page numbers given you can quickly locate the species in question.

To use these keys, select a good specimen and progress through the listed options the key offers. If the answer to the first part of a choice is "yes", move on to the name or number indicated; if "no" when only one choice is offered, move to the next number. Eventually you will reach the genus (or selection of genera) to which your species belongs. In winter, there is nothing to prevent you using the broadleaf key on fallen or dried leaves or using the leafless shoot key while the shoots are still leafy.

Learn to use the keys with a species already familiar to you. With practice you will find that their use together with detailed observation in the field will greatly improve your knowledge of trees and your ability to identify them.

Preliminary key

1   **a** Tree in leaf   ▷ **2**
     b Tree not in leaf   **Key C**

2   **a** Leaf needle- or scale-like; veins   **Key A**
     absent or (more rarely) parallel
     b Main veins branched, reticular   **Key B**
     c Leaf veins parallel, leaves more
     than 30 cm **Cordyline** 188 or
     Trachycarpus 188

Key A Conifer trees

1   **a** Lvs broad (over 4 mm), vns
     parallel   ▷ **2**
     b Lvs narrow or scale-like   ▷ **3**

2   **a** Lvs broadest at base, hard, sharp
     Araucaria 24
     b Lvs broadest at apex, soft, lobed,
     rounded **Gingko** 21

3   **a** Lvs set singly, in opp prs or
     whorls of 3   ▷ **4**
     b Lvs set spirally, singly or in
     bundles of 2–5   ▷ **8**

4   **a** Lvs linear, in fern-like fronds;
     new buds set below side shoots
     Metasequoia 38
     b Lvs scale- or awl-like   ▷ **5**

5   **a** Fruit berry-like; lvs set in 2s or 3s
     Juniperus 34
     b Fr a cone, lvs always paired   ▷ **6**

6   **a** Foliage in flat sprays   ▷ **7**
     b Foliage in 3-D sprays **Cupressus**
     25

7   **a** Cone rounded x **Cupressocyparis**
     27 or **Chamaecyparis** 28
     b Cone flask-shaped **Thuja/Biota**
     32, **Thujopsis** 33 or **Calocedrus** 34

8   Lvs long (10–15 cm), in spaced
     whorls **Sciadopitys** 39

9   **a** Lvs thin-textured, set in fern-like
     fronds **Taxodium** 37
     b Lvs not as above   ▷ **10**

10   **a** Sh not green (except when very
     young)   ▷ **11**
     b Sh green or yellow-green for at
     least 2 yrs   ▷ **16**

11   Lvs in bundles of 2, 3 or 5 **Pinus** 60

12   **a** Lvs in rosettes on 2nd yr and
     older shs   ▷ **13**
     b Lvs always single, spaced along
     shs   ▷ **14**

13 a Lvs soft, turning yellow in autumn; cones have persistent, open scales *Larix* 52
b Lvs hard; cones with deciduous scales *Cedrus* 50

14 Lvs set on prominent pegs projecting from shoot *Picea* 56 or (more rarely) *Tsuga* 58

15 a Cones small (under 3 cm), pendulous; buds very small (under 2 mm), rounded *Tsuga* 58
b Cones over 3 cm, pendulous, persistent, with exserted, trident bracts; *Pseudotsuga* 49
c Cones erect, over 5 cm, with deciduous scales *Abies* 41

16 a Lvs flat in x-section, parted on sh ▷ **17**
b Lvs round in x-section ▷ **19**

17 Bark thick, very soft *Sequoia* 37

18 a Lvs spine-tipped, very sharp to touch *Torreya* 22
b Lvs softer *Taxus* 22, *Podocarpus* 23 or *Saxegothaea* 23

19 a Lvs short (4–7 mm), pointed, dotted with stomata; bark thick, soft *Sequoiadendron* 36
b Lvs longer (to 1.5 cm), less adpressed; bark thin, hard, stringy *Cryptomeria* 39

Key B Broadleaf trees
An asterisk indicates that at least some species in the genus are evergreen

1 a Lvs in opp or nearly opp prs on sh ▷ **2**
b Lvs alt on sh ▷ **12**
c Lvs in whorls of 3, or both opp and alt *Lagerstroemia* 181, *Fraxinus* (rarely) or *Catalpa* 187

2 a Lvs compound ▷ **3**
b Lvs simple ▷ **4**

3 a Lvs pinnately compound *Euodia* 152, *Acer* 154, *Eucryphia*★ 171 or *Fraxinus* 182
b Lvs palmately compound *Acer* (rarely) 154 or *Aesculus* 166

4 a Lvs toothed or lobed ▷ **5**
b Lf margins entire (or with 1–2 prs of large teeth) ▷ **8**

5 Lvs lobed or lobulate *Acer*★ 154

6 Lvs thick, leathery, dark green *Eucryphia*★ 171 or *Phillyrea*★ 186

7 a Lvs narrowly oval; sh squarish *Euonymus* 152
b Lvs ovate with cordate bases; sh rounded, brown *Cercidiphyllum* 115

8 a Lvs leathery, evergreen, glaucous or glossy above ▷ **9**
b Lvs not leathery, deciduous ▷ **11**

9 a Lvs willow-like, felted white below *Olea*★ 185
b Lvs glabrous ▷ **10**

10 a Lvs same both sides, glaucous *Eucalyptus*★ 174
b Lvs not same both surfaces, glossy above *Ligustrum*★ 185

11 a Lvs less than 10 cm, veins curve parallel to margins *Cornus* 176
b Lvs more than 10 cm *Paulownia* 186 or *Catalpa* 187

12 a Lvs simple ▷ **20**
b Lvs pinnate ▷ **13**
c Lvs bipinnate *Gleditsia* 146, *Acacia*★ 147 or *Koelreuteria* 171

13 Lvs always comprise 3 lflts *Laburnum* 148

14 Pith chambered, not solid *Juglans* 84 or *Pterocarya* 85

15 Terminal lflt or 3 terminal lflts largest *Carya* 86

16 a Bud hidden in base of petiole ▷ **17**
b Bud not so hidden ▷ **18**

17 a Sh round, smooth, green, yellow or paler *Gleditsia* 146, *Sophora* 147 or *Rhus* 150
b Sh ridged, brown *Robinia* 146

18 a Lflts entire or with 1–3 prs of teeth at base *Ailanthus* 149 or *Rhus* 150
b Lflts toothed ▷ **19**

19 a Toothing regular *Sorbus* 124 or *Rhus* 150
b Toothing very coarse *Koelreuteria* 171

20 Lvs have truncate bases, indented apexes *Liriodendron* 119

21 Lvs concentrated at sh tip, fewer along sh; fruit an acorn *Quercus*★

13

22 Bk in upper crown smooth; peeling orange and yellow-pink *Arbutus*★ 178

23 a Lf margins entire, toothless ▷ **24**
    b Lvs toothed or lobed ▷ **31**

24 Lvs same both sides, pendulous *Eucalyptus*★ 174

25 Bk brown, flaking to yellow and pink *Parrotia* 120

26 a Lf margins wavy or crinkled ▷ **27**
    b Lf margins flat ▷ **28**

27 a Lvs very glossy, dark green above *Diospyros* 179
    b Lvs pale green, slightly glossy *Pittosporum*★ 165
    c Veins impressed, pubescent below *Salix* 79

28 Lvs orbicular *Cercis* 145

29 Lvs have vns curving parallel to margin *Cornus* 176

30 a Lvs elliptic to obovate *Salix* 79, *Magnolia*★ 116, *Cotoneaster*★ 123 or *Nyssa* 172
    b Lvs lanceolate *Embrothrium*★ 119, *Cotoneaster*★ 125 or *Pyrus* 133

31 a Lvs lobed ▷ **32**
    b Lvs toothed or lobulate, not lobed ▷ **36**

32 a Vns arise at lf base (palmate vns) ▷ **33**
    b Vns arise along midrib (pinnate vns) *Crataegus* 122 or *Sorbus* 124

33 Bud hidden in hollow base of petiole *Platanus* 153

34 Lf uns densely hairy *Populus* 73

35 a Sinuses obtuse, rounded *Morus* 113, *Ficus* 114 or *Kalopanax* 175
    b Sinuses acute *Liquidambar* 120 or *Kalopanax* 175

36 Margins have spine-like teeth *Castanea* 105 or *Ilex*★ 151

37 Sh has bristly, glandular hrs *Corylus* 92

38 a Lvs rounded ovate, more than 4 cm, bases cordate or oblique *Tilia* 168 or *Davidia* 173
    b Lvs less than 4 cm, not as above ▷ **39**

39 Lvs deltoid or orbicular; petiole flattened or lf uns "painted" white **Populus** 73

40 a Pith finely chambered, fr 4–winged **Halesia** 181
b Pith solid ▷ **41**

41 a Vns deeply impressed **Salix** 79, **Carpinus** 93, **Nothofagus** 96 or **Parrotia** 120
b Vns not deeply impressed ▷ **42**

42 Petiole has 2 (1–4) glands near lf blade **Prunus** 134

43 Lvs lanceolate **Salix** 79

44 Lf uns has silvery white pubescence **Sorbus** 124 or **Malus** 130

45 Margins crinkled or wavy **Alnus** 90, **Fagus** 94, **Stewartia** 172 or **Styrax** 180

46 Lvs obliquely based, doubly serrate **Ulmus** 107

47 Lvs oblong-obovate, 5–15 cm, mostly stalkless, minutely toothed, downy both sides **Mespilus** 123

48 Fruit a persistent, ovoid, woody cone-like catkin **Alnus** 90

49 Fruit a cylindrical or ovoid catkin, scales deciduous **Betula** 87

50 Lvs dark, shiny green, elliptic-oblong, fruit strawberry-like **Arbutus★** 178

51 Teeth deep, single, in 12 or less prs **Zelkova** 112 or **Ulmus** 107

52 Bark silvery-grey, fluted; lf vns parallel, impressed **Carpinus** 93

53 Shoots have spines; fruit berry-like **Crataegus** 122

54 a Flowers and fruits in umbels **Malus** 130
b Flowers and fruits in racemes ▷ **55**

55 Lvs nearly round or elliptic, densely pubescent and glaucous below **Styrax** 180

56 a Lvs under 5 cm, dull; fls in spring **Amelanchier** 121
b Lvs over 5 cm, glossy; fls in autumn **Oxydendrum** 179

Key C Leafless winter shoots

1 **a** Buds in opp prs or whorls of 3 ▷ **2**
  b Buds alt along sh ▷ **11**

2 Lf scars set above buds; bark fibrous, red-brown *Metasequoia* 38

3 **a** Buds with 2 outer scales ▷ **4**
  b Buds with sev outer scales or none ▷ **5**

4 **a** Buds elongated *Cornus* 176
  b Buds stalked *Acer* 154
  c Buds pointed; sh winged or ribbed *Lagerstroemia* 181

5 Sh squarish, green for 1st winter *Euonymus* 152

6 **a** Terminal bud lacking ▷ **7**
  b Terminal bud present ▷ **8**

7 **a** Sh slender; buds 3–6 mm, crimson-brown *Cercidiphyllum* 115
  b Sh stouter, over 5 mm; buds small, less than 2 mm *Paulownia* 186 or *Catalpa* 187

8 Buds naked *Euodia* 152

9 **a** Buds have 4–8 pubescent scales *Fraxinus* 182
  b Buds have 8+ scales ▷ **10**

10 **a** Sh stout, buds large *Aesculus* 166
  b Sh less stout, buds under 8 mm, not resinous *Acer* 154

11 **a** Shs have spines ▷ **12**
  b Shs do not have spines ▷ **13**

12 **a** Spines brown, curved, paired either side of bud *Robinia* 146
  b Spines stout, 3-pronged, often on bole *Gleditsia* 146
  c Spines single with buds set at bases *Crataegus* 122, *Mespilus* 123, *Malus* 130, *Pyrus* 133, *Prunus* 134 (rarely in most except *Crataegus*)

13 **a** ♂ catkins exposed over winter at twig end ▷ **14**
  b Not as above ▷ **16**

14 Buds stalked; fr a woody, cone-like catkin, persistent *Alnus* 90

15 **a** Sh has bristly hrs; fr a nut *Corylus* 92
  b Sh has no bristly hrs; fr a catkin *Betula* 87

16 **a** Buds naked ▷ **17**
    b Buds have scales ▷ **20**

17 **a** Pith chambered *Pterocarya* 85
    b Pith solid ▷ **18**

18 **a** Sh ribbed, brown *Robinia* 146
    b Sh round ▷ **19**

19 **a** Sh green *Gleditsia* 146
    b Sh brown or brownish *Rhus* 150

20 **a** Buds have single scale ▷ **21**
    b Buds with 2+ scales ▷ **24**

21 **a** Lf scar around bud ▷ **22**
    b Lf scar only below bud ▷ **23**

22 **a** Bud conic, single *Platanus* 153
    b Buds adpressed, usually 2+
together *Styrax* 180

23 **a** Terminal bud large, pinched at
base *Magnolia* 116
    b Terminal lacking, other buds
conic, adpressed *Salix* 79

24 Winter buds clustered at sh end; on
rest of sh are spaced, fewer, smaller
Quercus 98

25 **a** Bud single, central on sh short ▷ **26**
    b Buds multiple *or* shs not short ▷ **27**

26 **a** Sh ribbed; fr a persistent cone
Larix 52
    b Sh round; fr a drupe *Gingko* 21
27 Bud spindle-shaped, pointed, 2 cm
Fagus 94

28 Fr 4-winged *Halesia* 181

29 Pith chambered *Juglans* 84

30 Bud acute, adpressed *Carpinus* 93
or *Nothofagus* 96

31 Bud resinous *Populus* 73 or *Sorbus*
124

32 **a** Bud stalked ▷ **33**
    b Bud sessile ▷ **34**

33 **a** Bark flakes to pink or yellow-
green below *Parrotia* 120
    b Bark tight, regularly ridged
Liriodendron 119

34 **a** Sh green or greenish ▷ **35**
    b Sh not as above ▷ **40**

35 **a** Sh green for 2+ years ▷ **36**

b Sh partially green or for only 1 yr ▷ **38**

36 Lf scar around bud *Gleditsia* 146 or *Sophora* 147

37 a Lf buds with 2 unequal scales *Tilia* 168
b Lf buds with 2+ scales *Laburnum* 148

38 a Bud large, over 5 mm *Carya* 86 or *Ficus* 114
b Bud under 5 mm ▷ **39**

39 a Bud yellow-green *Oxydendrum* 174
b Bud red-brown *Nyssa* 172
c Not as above *Prunus* 134

40 a Shs angled *Castanea* 107
b Shs with corky ridges or wings *Liquidambar* 120 or *Ulmus* 107
c Sh round ▷ **41**

41 a Sh over 5 mm ▷ **42**
b Sh under 5 mm ▷ **43**

42 a Buds large; sh has prickles *Kalopanax* 175
b Buds small; sh without prickles *Ailanthus* 149

43 a Buds with 2 or 3 scales ▷ **44**
b Buds with 4+ scales ▷ **46**

44 Buds with 3 scales; bark black, fissured into squares *Diospyros* 179

45 a Sh straight, pale reddish or coppery *Koelreuteria* 171
b Sh zig-zags *Tilia* 168

46 Bud ovoid, pointed, shiny red or chestnut brown *Morus* 113, *Sorbus* 124, *Pyrus* 133, *Prunus* 134, *Davidia* 173

47 a Buds in 2s or more above lf scar ▷ **48**
b Buds set singly above lf scar ▷ **49**

48 a Bud silky; bark flaking *Stewartia* 172
b Sh dark red; fr a pod hanging from old wood *Cercis* 145

49 Bark red brown, stringy; twigs reddish, supple *Taxodium* 37

50 Bud small, less than 2 mm *Ulmus* 107, *Zelkova* 112, *Halesia* 181

The conifers

The Gymnospermae, known colloquially as the conifers, belong to three different botanical groups or orders, the Gingko group, the Yew group and the true conifers. Britain has only three native conifers, the Scots pine, the Yew and the Juniper, many other species which are now familiar having been introduced from Europe, Asia and America. The simple upright habit, making good timber, and the fact that they can grow fast on poor soils and in harsh climates have made conifers ideal for widespread forestry cultivation.

The fundamental botanical difference between conifers and all others plants is that their ovules, which develop into seeds, are carried naked. This gives the group their scientific name, the Gymnospermae, and distinguishes them from the Angiospermae or "enclosed ovule" trees, known as broadleaf trees. The ovules are borne on the scales of the female flower, an immature cone, which closes its scales after fertilization.

This is of little help with identification, however, and it is far better to examine other characteristics of growth, habit and fruit. Conifers in general have a strongly monopodal growth habit, with a single stem and much lighter, smaller side branches. Some do not maintain this character into old age and particularly in European larch and the silver firs one or two very heavy horizontal side branches may turn up at the ends and form competing leaders. Some of the yews also have a tendency to heavier branching; forking often occurs and one of the stems outpaces and suppresses the other.

a   b   c

The illustrations above show some points to look for when examining the superficially similar needles of most conifers. The spruce needle **a** has a pointed apex, is squarish in section, and is similar in appearance above and below. The Silver fir needle **b** and **c** is notched at the apex, much flatter, and has white bands on the underside which are in fact the stomata, pores which open and close as the light intensity and humidity vary. Conifer leaves are generally arranged helically along the shoot, although this is sometimes disguised when the leaves are twisted at the base and appear to be arranged pectinately, spreading either side of the shoot. In some species the leaves may be arranged on short shoots, most notably amongst the cedars, larches and gingko. Although still in a helix the leaves are compressed and appear to be a whorl with a central bud.

The seeds are ripe in the autumn six or eighteen months after fertilization, and the cone scales usually open, in dry weather, to release them on the wind. The seeds are tucked between the fertile and bract scales (left).

They are usually winged to assist in their distribution. The number of seeds per scale can vary from one to as many as twenty. In some conifers the seeds remain attached to the scales, which themselves separate from the cone and fall.

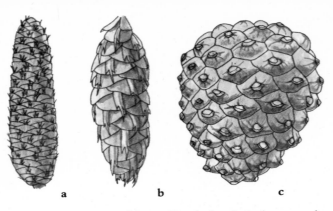

a   b   c

The colloquial name of the conifers derives from the cones, the hard woody fruits with overlapping scales which bear their seeds. They vary enormously from one genus to another, and are perhaps the best means of identification; the illustrations on this page show some points to look for. The silver fir cone **a** sits erect on the shoot, and is long and cylindrical. It is also distinctive because of the bracts, which are reflexed, and stand out from the body of the cone. This is one of the cones which are rarely found whole on the ground, because their scales are deciduous, falling to the ground and leaving a long bare stalk or "candle" on the tree. The Douglas fir cone **b** is equally distinctive in its growth, as it always hangs from the shoot. It is also shorter and more ovoid in shape, and has prominent bracts, which are three-pointed. The pine cone **c**, with its rounded base, pointed tip and triangular scales, is often imagined to be typical of all cones, although it only reaches this form after eighteen months. A feature of these cones is the blunt projection known as an umbo borne on the outside of each scale. Pine cones are often asymmetrical, something comparatively rare in other genera.

d   e   f

The Juniper fruit **d** is quite unlike that of any other conifer, in that it is not really a cone at all but a soft fleshy berry. As the fruit takes two or three years to ripen the green immature fruit and the ripe blue ones can usually be found on the same tree. The female flowers begin life like all other conifers, as open scales, but they mature into hard round berries, recognizable by the scars and blunt points left from what were their scales. The Western red cedar cone **e** is unusual in not having overlapping scales, but ones which separate from the base. The centre of the cone is leathery and ovoid, visible behind the few spreading scales. The cone of the Coast redwood **f** is much smaller and very knobbly, with the scales presenting a diamond-shaped surface. These scales each have a central hollow, and as they ripen from green to brown they shrink and separate. The seeds, which can easily be obtained by shaking a newly ripened cone, vary considerably in size and appearance. The conifers usually bear their seeds two per scale.

Gingko family Gingkoaceae

Gingko

Gingko biloba

30 m. Crown *columnar, broadening with age.*
Branches *short, numerous, dipping when old.* **Bark** *ridged, fissured*

Buds *set spirally around shoots*

Leaves *variable, from 6–12 cm, set in whorls of 2–5 on short, slow growing, older shoots; larger, set singly on new shoots.*
Blades *open pale yellow-green, golden in autumn*

Leaf *ribbed, divided into 2 or more lobes on soft shoots; those on long shoots may be undivided*

Veins *straight, parallel, non-dividing*

The Gingko is the only survivor of a group of trees that flourished some 200 million years ago. Its primitive ancestry shows in its regular, dichotomous (forked) venation and the rudimentary method by which its ovule is fertilized. As in the ferns, this is by free-swimming sperm cells and fertilization often occurs *after* its ovoid, yellow fruit, found only on female trees, has fallen. This emits a putrid stench once its fleshy coat begins to rot. The Gingko is only native to a remote part of China where it was adopted as a sacred tree by Buddhist monks who carried it to Japan. From there it was introduced to Europe and America in the eighteenth century. Specimens planted then still survive and an immunity to air pollution and most pests and diseases makes Gingko ideal for towns. Its name, "Maidenhair tree", is based on the similarity of its leaves to those of Maidenhair fern.

21

Yew family Taxaceae

Yews are usually dioecious; females produce solitary seeds in a fleshy aril. Leaves are set spirally or in pectinate ranks.

Yew

Taxus baccata

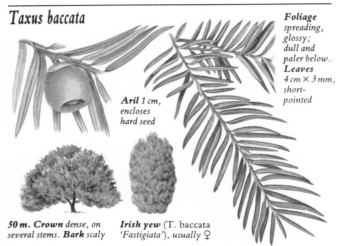

Foliage *spreading, glossy; dull and paler below.* **Leaves** *4 cm × 3 mm, short-pointed*

Aril *1 cm, encloses hard seed*

50 m. Crown *dense, on several stems.* **Bark** *scaly*

Irish yew (T. baccata 'Fastigiata'), *usually* ♀

A widespread species native to chalk upland and shady, broad-leaved woods, the Yew is noted for its longevity — many in churchyards may be 1,000 years old — and its scarlet "berries" which ripen in September and are distributed by birds.

California nutmeg

Torreya californica

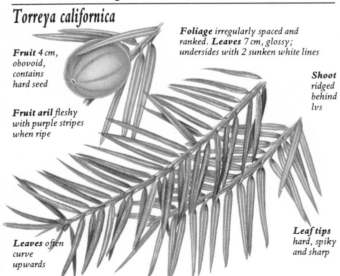

Foliage *irregularly spaced and ranked.* **Leaves** *7 cm, glossy; undersides with 2 sunken white lines*

Fruit *4 cm, obovoid, contains hard seed*

Fruit aril *fleshy with purple stripes when ripe*

Shoot *ridged behind lvs*

Leaves *often curve upwards*

Leaf tips *hard, spiky and sharp*

An open-crowned tree with spreading branches and stout shoots, this species reaches 15 metres and its fruit has seeds resembling those of the true nutmeg. Japanese nutmeg (*T. nucifera*) has shorter and decurrent needles.

Podocarp family Podocarpaceae

These species come mainly from the southern hemisphere and carry cones with fleshy scales and less regular foliage than the yew family. Male and female flowers may appear on the same tree.

Prince Albert yew

Saxegothaea conspicua

15 m. Crown has rounded apex. **Branches** droop. **Leaf** 2 cm, matt; white bands below

Leaf tips abruptly pointed

Foliage hard, curved, set closely but unevenly

Cone 1 cm, comprising 3 whorls of 3 fleshy scales. **Bole** often bends

A Chilean tree which was named after Queen Victoria's consort, this differs from Yew in its fruit, irregular foliage and leaf undersides while its less dense, pendulous shoots distinguish it from *P. andinus*.

Chile yew

Podocarpus andinus

Foliage dense; bunched at shoot tips, elsewhere irregularly pectinate

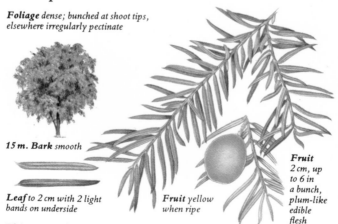

15 m. Bark smooth

Leaf to 2 cm with 2 light bands on underside

Fruit yellow when ripe

Fruit 2 cm, up to 6 in a bunch, plum-like edible flesh

This tree of variable habit is sometimes confused with Prince Albert yew but is closer to Willow podocarp (*P. salignus*) which has 5–10 cm leaves parted in two ranks and a red-brown shaggy bark. Both these podocarps are native to Chile.

Chile pine family Araucariaceae

This family comprises two genera and 36 species, all natives of the southern hemisphere. Trees are either male or female, the female ones carrying globose or ovoid cones containing many scales, each with one seed. Leaves are hard with parallel venation and are usually broad and arranged spirally.

Monkey puzzle

Araucaria araucana

25 m. Crown *domed or conical, variable in depth.* **Bole** *very straight with occasional suckers.* **Bark** *dark grey, fissured, with old branch scars*

Branches *in whorls, horizontal near apex of crown, drooping elsewhere, upturned at tips.* **Foliage** *remains green for 10–15 years, persisting after dying and turning brown*

♂ **cone** *6–10 cm, green at first then brown, dry, papery, hanging in clusters of 1–6 near branch tips, persisting 1 year*

Leaves *4 × 1 cm, set spirally, interlocking round shoot, hard, leathery, sharply tipped, with parallel veins*

♀ **cone** *large, 15 cm, ripens to brown in 2nd autumn when 4 cm seeds released as it breaks up*

Indigenous to Chile where its tasty seeds were once an important food of the Araucano tribe, the Monkey puzzle was first introduced to Europe in 1794 and its common name, alluding to the problems its sharp foliage would give potential climbers, was first used in 1834. The Norfolk Island pine (*A. heterophylla*) has softer, awl-shaped leaves. It can grow in the open in warm areas but is more common as an indoor plant.

Cypress family Cupressaceae

Trees in the Cypress family are distinguished from other conifers, except *Metasequoia* (p 38), by their paired or ternate leaves. Those of juvenile plants are always awl-shaped, a condition retained by some species and many cultivars. Adult leaves are mostly small, scale-like and adpressed. Members of Cupressaceae carry male and female flowers on the same or separate trees and three types of cone are produced: those of *Cupressus* (pp 25–6) and *Chamaecyparis* (pp 28–31) are globose or ellipsoid with peltate scales; those of *Juniperus* (pp 34–5) have unique fleshy scales which are fused together. All other Cypress genera—including *Thuja* (pp 32–3), *Thujopsis* (p 33) and *Calocedrus* (p 34)—have larger cones with woody scales hinged at their bases.

Monterey cypress

Cupressus macrocarpa

Young crown columnar conic with erect leader

'Lutea' 26 m, perhaps hardier than the type. **Foliage** thicker, grows more slowly, greener when planted in shade

35 m. Habit usually this shape when mature but can broaden and become flat-topped

Leaves small, 2 mm, scale-like

Branches ascend at base, level near apex. **Bark** ridged

Foliage slender but set densely, lemon-scented when crushed. **Shoots** forward-pointing, almost cylindrical, covered by lvs

Foliage thicker, shorter on older trees; salt-resistant

Cone to 4 cm when mature, has 8 or 10 peltate scales

This species is found wild on the coast of California and was widely planted as a hedge tree although it has now been largely superseded in that role by the hardier and faster growing Leyland cypress (p 27). A fungal disease, *Seiridium* (= *Coryneum*) *cardinale*, attacks Monterey cypress as well as Italian cypress (p 26) and can prove fatal.

Italian cypress

Cupressus sempervirens

Cone 4 cm, ovoid, ripening from green over 18 months. **Scales** are 5-sided and sinuate

Foliage dense. **Shoots** branch repeatedly in all planes, unlike Chamae-cyparis

Leaves 1 mm, scale-like, resembling C. macrocarpa *but sharper, flatter*

20 m. Crown columnar, often prone to fungal disease (see p 25); spreads wider with level brs in wild

This is the classic cypress, native to Greece and the Balkans and now widely distributed throughout Mediterranean countries. Cedar of Goa (*C. lusitanica*), from Mexico, has a broader crown, smaller, glaucous cones and spreading, pointed leaves.

Smooth cypress

Cupressus glabra

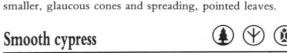

Foliage open, branching almost at 90°

Bark smooth, flaked, can be cherry-red

Cone 15–25 mm, often clustered and persistent, bloomed at first. **Scales** have low, curved spikes

20 m. Crown conical or ovoid, fairly dense with blunt apex. **Branches** ascend. **Branchlets** horizontal. **Bole** short

Distinguished by its bark, this tree is being increasingly planted as an ornamental. It was once classified· as a cultivar of Arizona cypress (*C. arizonica*) whose bark is much rougher.

Cupressocyparis leylandii

Cone
(when present)
3 cm,
globular,
brown

Foliage *dark green or grey, in irregular, flattish planes (with neither the truly flat sprays of* Chamaecyparis *nor the more radial arrangement of* Cupressus*); less dense near leader.*
Shoots *branch repeatedly.* **Leaves** *slightly incurved with ridged glands.*
Growth *fast, can exceed 1 m a year*

40 m. Crown *dense, columnar with conic or rounded conic apex.* **Branches** *ascend steeply.* **Leader** *leans slightly, not drooping as in Lawson cypress (pp 30–31).* **Bark** *initially smooth, then ridged becoming stringy*

'Castlewellan' is extremely vigorous and its foliage, arranged in plumes, turns bronze-green in winter

Leyland cypress is a naturally spontaneous hybrid of Monterey cypress (p 25) and Nootka cypress (p 29) and the qualities inherited from its parents—the vigorous growth rate of the first and the adaptable durability of the second—have made this tree unbeatable as a hedge conifer. Several clones are now marketed. The most popular, 'Haggerston Grey', was first raised in 1888 but two recently introduced golden forms, 'Castlewellan' and 'Robinson's Gold' are becoming increasingly acceptable. Leyland rarely sets viable seed but plants are easily raised from cuttings.

Hinoki cypress

Chamaecyparis obtusa

Foliage in very flat sprays

Foliage in fan-like, feathery sprays. **Leaves** small, 2 mm, in blunt pairs, with white scale joints on undersides

25 m. Crown columnar, conic: **Branches** level then ascending. **Bole** straight. **Bark** fissured

Cone 1 cm

This native of Japan can be distinguished from other "false" cypresses by its blunt, incurved leaves and larger, round cones. 'Crippsii', a popular cultivar, has bright, golden–yellow foliage which darkens to green inside the crown.

Sawara cypress

Chamaecyparis pisifera

Cone small, 5 mm, densely clustered, ripening unevenly to dark brown. **Scales** (10–12) spiked

Foliage dense, in flat, upturned sprays, darkening with age and with bright white leaf bases below

Leaves of many Sawara cultivars are always awl-shaped and set in pairs. Those of **'Squarrosa'** (right) 6 mm long while leaves of **'Plumosa'** are half this size

Leaves small, 3 mm, adpressed, in similarly sized pairs, fine-pointed, incurved

Native to Japan, this tree has distinctively small cones and as the type is far less common than its numerous cultivars. These can be divided into those with pendulous foliage such as 'Filifera' and those whose awl–shaped leaves are set at about 45° like 'Plumosa' or approximately at right angles as on 'Squarrosa'.

Nootka cypress

Chamaecyparis nootkatensis

Leading shoot *leans*

Crown *is extremely regular*

Cone 1 cm, *globular, with large scale spikes, green with blue bloom, ripens brown over 2 years*

Foliage *very pendulous, in thick, flat, alternate sprays.* **Leaves** *2–3 mm, hard, in equal-sized pairs*

30 cm. Bark *stringy, peels*

One of the parents of Leyland cypress (p27), Nootka cypress, from Alaska, is easily recognized by its hanging branchlets and the hooked spines of its cones. Its 'Pendula' form has very pendulous foliage, shorter, upturned branches and 2 cm cones.

White cypress

Chamaecyparis thyoides

Foliage *very slender, 1 mm, short, fern-like, angular green or bluish-grey sprays.* **Cones** *set on small branchlets*

Leaves *often have central resin glands and carry prominent white marks near bases, particularly on undersides*

Leaves *very small, down to 1 mm, acutely pointed, incurved and close-pressed but freer on vigorous growth.* **Shoot** *becomes brown in 2nd year*

15 m. Crown *columnar or broad conic.* **Branches** *short.* **Bark** *stringy.* **Cone** *6 mm, glaucous blue-purple ripening brown*

The slow-growing White cypress is native to swamps along the eastern American seaboard. Its wood is so durable trees buried for decades have proved sufficiently strong to use for making roof shingles. Its botanical name comes from a resemblance to Thuja (pp32–3) and its common name from the paleness of its foliage.

Chamaecyparis lawsoniana

20–35 m, to 50 m in wild. **Crown** regular in young trees, less so in mature ones. **Stem** often forked. **Foliage** dense, pendulous, becoming spaced in old trees. **Leader** and new shoots always droop. **Terminals** wispy, unbranched near tips

Cones 8 mm, globose, ripening from green or blue-green to dark brown. **Scales** (8) have short central spikes

Bark smooth, ridged then scaly, dark red-brown, purplish on older trees

♂ **flowers** terminate weakest branchlets

Foliage flat, fern-like. **Leaves** grouped in pairs: lateral ones keel-shaped, facing pairs smaller, adpressed. Each leaf has central translucent gland. Between leaf scales, stomata form thin, white lines. Especially clear on foliage underside; give best identification

The Lawson cypress is native to a small area on the Oregon-California border and as a forest species is characterized by a uniform crown of dense, pendent foliage. An expedition sponsored by the Scottish nurseryman Peter Lawson, discovered it there in 1854 and the vast array of hardy and easily propagated cultivars raised since then—some 250—have made this "false" cypress the most common ornamental conifer now grown. Its varieties can be divided into a group with vivid foliage, one with distinctly shaped habits and a third whose long, awl-like leaves resemble the juvenile leaves of the seedling.

Some cultivars of Lawson cypress

1 'Allumii': 20 m; compact habit, soft foliage. **2 'Columnaris'**: 10 m; dense, consistently narrow crown. **3 'Erecta'**: 25 m; first Lawson cypress cultivar, raised in 1855 from seeds of a Californian type; much-forked crown. **4 'Fletcherii'**: 16 m; juvenile foliage, often on several stems; multiple leaders.

5 'Intertexta': 25 m; foliage sparse, dark and bloomed, sprays pendent. **6 'Lutea'**: 16 m; short, pendulous branchlets; older interior foliage darker. **7 'Stewartii'**: 16 m; ascending branches with sprays decurved below shoot. **8 'Wissellii'**: 25 m; spaced foliage arranged in dense, radiating "spires".

Western red cedar

Thuja plicata

**40 m.
Crown**
conic,
broadening
with age.
Tip erect

Cone 1 cm,
with 10–12
scales, has
hooked tip,
flask-
shaped
when
closed

Seed 5 mm,
winged,
notched

Branches
light, even,
upswept at
ends, can
layer in old
trees

Foliage
aromatic

Bole
fluted

Bark dull,
stringy

Foliage flattened,
overlapping. **Leaves**
incurved, glossy, paler
below with whitish streaks

From the Pacific coast of North America, this majestic tree has a light but very even crown and is planted for its light and durable timber, often used for roofing shingles. Japanese thuja (*T. standishii*) has lighter, blunt, glanded leaves which smell of lemons.

Chinese thuja

Biota orientalis

**15 m.
Crown** on
several
ascending
stems, less
dense at base

Cone 1.5 cm. **Foliage** in
flat, erect sprays. **Leaves**
same green below

Bark
dull,
fissured,
stringy

Seed
6 mm,
rounded,
wingless

This species is often included in the Thuja genus and although its foliage bears some resemblance to that of the true thujas, it differs from them in its broader, glaucous cones which have fewer, strongly hooked scales and large, round, wingless seeds.

White cedar

Thuja occidentalis

Cone *1 cm, upright, on stronger shoots, often very frequent, with rounded scale tips, ripening brown by autumn*

Foliage *in twisted, erect sprays when young, otherwise hanging unhealthily*

Glands *translucent*

Foliage *smells of apples*

Leaves *acutely tipped*

Leaves *small, 2.5 mm, thick, uniformly paler and glandular below*

Small and slow-growing, this species was introduced to Europe from eastern North America, perhaps as early as 1536. Its smooth cones and foliage underside are distinctive. 'Lutea' has a denser crown and stronger branches whose tips bear golden leaves.

Hiba

Thujopsis dolabrata

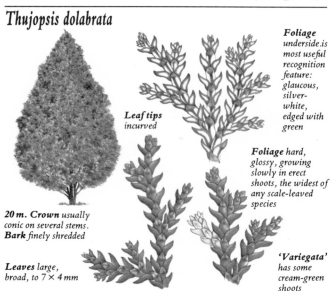

Foliage *underside is most useful recognition feature: glaucous, silver-white, edged with green*

Leaf tips *incurved*

Foliage *hard, glossy, growing slowly in erect shoots, the widest of any scale-leaved species*

20 m. Crown *usually conic on several stems.* **Bark** *finely shredded*

Leaves *large, broad, to 7 × 4 mm*

'Variegata' *has some cream-green shoots*

This Japanese tree rarely grows on a single stem and carries rounded, blue-grey cones. The leaf undersides of Korean thuja (*Thuja koraiensis*) are also — sometimes completely — silvery glaucous but its foliage is softer and it has typical *Thuja* cones.

Incense cedar

Calocedrus decurrens

35 m. Crown *columnar and slim in cultivation, far broader when wild.* **Branches** *short*

Foliage *dense, in irregular flat sprays, yellower beneath.* **Leaves** *to 12 mm, in unequal pairs with facial ones shorter*

Cone scales *hooked*

Cones *long, narrow, 2–3 cm, with only middle 2 scales carrying seeds, red-brown when fully ripe.* **Bark** *thick, furrowed, scaling*

A native of Oregon and California, Incense cedar can be confused with the much more common 'Erecta' cultivar of Lawson cypress (p31) but is distinguished by its irregular foliage, short, upswept branches and the yellower undersides of its leaves. Its fragrant timber gives the tree its name.

Juniper

Juniperus communis

Shoots *very slender.* **Leaves** *short, 1 cm, sharp*

8 m. Crown *small, usually spreading, shrubby, but cultivars very variable*

Leaves *concave, set in whorls of 3*

Leaves *glaucous white on inner surfaces.* **Cone** *1 cm, green for 2–3 years, blue-black when ripe*

Juniper will grow on both acid and alkaline sites and has a very wide distribution throughout the northern hemisphere. The bright green leaves of Temple juniper (*J. rigida*) are softer and longer while Alerce (*Fitzroya cuppressoides*) has spreading blue-green leaves with two silver bands on each side.

Pencil cedar

Juniperus virginiana

20 m. Crown ragged, open, conic when tree young

Branches upswept or spreading

Cones 5 mm, rounded or ovoid, glaucous, ripening in first year

Bark peels in strips. **Bole** often fluted

Juvenile leaves 14 mm

Shoots very slender, 4-angled. **Leaves** mainly scale-like, pointed, in opposite pairs. **Juvenile leaves** set at tips and bases of sprays

Pencil juniper, the tallest of the junipers, is indigenous to eastern North America and provides useful timber, especially for pencils. While not dissimilar to Chinese juniper, its finer foliage, *paired* juvenile leaves, *pointed* scale leaves and much smaller cones clearly distinguish it.

Chinese juniper

Juniperus chinensis

20 m. Crown of best trees (such as 'Aurea' shown here) dense and conic, one-stemmed

Branches ascend gently

Cone 6 mm, lumpy, glaucous

♂ *flowers*

Bole often deeply fluted. **Bark** peels in narrow, stringy strips

Scale leaves small, blunt. **Awl leaves** 1 cm, prickly, set in both 2s and 3s

Chinese juniper is the most common juniper growing as a tree and of its several cultivars, 'Aurea' is the most popular and produces masses of male flowers. Drooping juniper (*J. recurva*) has dry, pendent foliage which rustles when shaken; its softer, green, adpressed awl leaves are set in threes.

Redwood family Taxodiaceae

This ancient group of large, beautiful trees comprises 10 genera from North America, eastern Asia and Tasmania. Its members usually have evergreen leaves, which are flat, linear or awl-shaped and set spirally along the shoot, and globular woody cones, whose peltate scales are also arranged spirally. All redwoods are monoecious. They have thick barks that are red-brown and fibrous. Some genera are deciduous.

Wellingtonia

Sequoiadendron giganteum

Leaves
small, to 7 mm, awl-shaped, hard, dotted with white stomata

Foliage
blue-grey when young then shiny, dark green on older shoots

Shoot stout, initially covered by leaves, later developing grey-brown fissures

Cone
large, 6 cm, 35–40 scales, green for 2 years, then brown

Branches
have tips upswept

50 m. Crown often has rounded apex. **Bole** tapers, fluted. **Bark** often dimpled by Tree-creepers using it for winter roosting

Bark very thick, to 30 cm, soft and resilient, can withstand punching

Wellingtonia is the world's largest (though not the tallest) living phenomenon and is native to 72 groves on the high, western slopes of the Californian Sierra Nevadas where it was first discovered in 1841. The largest individual there, named "General Sherman", is 83 m tall, has a trunk diameter of 10 m and weighs 1,000 tonnes, yet must have developed over the centuries from a seed weighing a mere 5 milligrammes. Such specimens may live for 4,000 years although the average age of native species is only a quarter of this. In Europe, growth rates have exceeded 50 m in a century. Wellingtonias have deep roots to withstand long, dry summers and their thick bark gives protection against forest fires.

California redwood

Sequoia sempervirens

Shoot *green.* **Strong shoot leaves** *small, 6–8 mm, scale-like, awl-shaped, adpressed around stem with tips incurved*

Side-shoot leaves *1–2 cm, tapering to hard apexes with 2 white bands below, set in flat sprays*

Cone. *3 cm.* **Scales** *(15–20) ripen in first season*

50 m. Crown *thin, columnar conic, becoming flat-topped.* **Bole** *straight, tapering*

Bark *thick, very soft, fibrous; bright red-brown on young trees, darker and fissured on old ones*

This redwood is the tallest tree in the world, reaching 112 m (the height of St Paul's Cathedral, London) in its native California where it thrives in the damp atmosphere of the narrow, coastal "fogbelt". Chinese fir (*Cunninghamia lanceolata*) has a similar bark but much longer, more broadly based leaves.

Swamp cypress

Taxodium distichum

Leaves *1–1.5 cm, set in 2 flat rows*

Foliage *on side-shoots falls in November*

Cone *3 cm, globular, green, ripening brown in first season*

Winter twig *has scars left by fallen deciduous shoots*

30 m. Crown *has domed apex.* **Bark** *fibrous.* **Aerial roots** *(pneumatophores) supply oxygen to trees growing in water-logged sites*

Sometimes confused with *Metasequoia* (p 38) from which it can be distinguished by its alternate foliage, this tree from the southern USA prefers waterside sites but grows well on any fairly moist soil. The closely related Pond cypress (*T. ascendens*) has erect, spiky shoots of shorter, radially arranged leaves.

Dawn redwood

Metasequoia glyptostroboides

Foliage *fern-like, bright yellow-green then darkening*

Shoots *opposite, deciduous when not bearing buds*

Bole *shown in cross-section below very deeply fluted, tapering*

Bark *bright orange- or red-brown, stringy*

Leaves *2–4 cm × 2 mm, opposite, soft, curved, in flat sprays*

30 m. Crown *sparse, narrow conic becoming columnar.* **Branches** *ascend.* **Foliage** *assumes exquisite autumnal hues*

Long thought to be extinct, this fine tree was located in south-eastern China as recently as 1941 since when its hardiness, the ease with which it propagates and a growth rate which can average a metre per annum have made it a popular ornamental. Its botanical name indicates affinities with *Sequoia* (p 37) and the rare, deciduous Chinese swamp cypress (*Glyptostrobus lineatus*) but it is more easily confused with Swamp cypress (p 37), whose similar foliage is also deciduous. The leaves and lateral shoots of Dawn redwood, however, are longer and *opposite*. It is unique in carrying its side-buds *below* its shoots and not in their axils.

Japanese cedar

Cryptomeria japonica

'Elegans' leaves *long, 2 cm, soft, spirally set, becoming red or bronze-brown in winter*

Cone *2 cm, globular, ripening in 1 season.* **Scales** *(20–40) each with 4–6 hooked spines*

Leaves *long, 1.5 cm, set spirally, turning slightly bronze in winter*

35 m. Crown *narrow conic, unevenly dense.* **Branches** *spaced, horizontal or billowing, tips upswept.* **Bark** *soft, fibrous, fissured, peeling on old trees*

As an introduced ornamental, this tree never reaches the heights it attains in its native China and Japan. The Tasmanian *Athrotaxis* species have similar cones but shorter leaves: King William pine (*A. selaginoides*) has hard, shiny leaves of 1 cm, Summit cedar (*A. laxifolia*) awl-like ones to 2 mm and Tasmanian cedar (*A. cupressoides*) adpressed scale leaves.

Japanese umbrella pine

Sciadopitys verticillata

20 m. Crown *narrow to broad conic.* **Branches** *short, upturned and spreading.* **Bark** *dark red-brown, peeling in strips*

Leaves *very long, 10–15 cm, fused in grooved pairs which glossy above and bright yellow below*

Foliage *set round shoots in whorls*

Native to the mountains of Japan, where it is an important timber tree, this species grows very slowly in European parks and large gardens. Its distinctive foliage of long and whorled, glossy "double" leaves distinguishes it from all other conifers and offers immediate identification.

Pine family Pinaceae

The Pine family is the most varied of all those groups of trees which bear cones. Besides the genus *Pinus* itself, the family also contains those of *Abies*, *Picea*, *Tsuga*, *Pseudotsuga* and *Larix* as well as *Pseudolarix*, *Cathaya* and *Keteleeria* (these latter three are fairly obscure Chinese genera and, because they are so seldom found elsewhere, not included in this book.)

Together, all the Pinaceae comprise well over 250 species, all of which are native to the northern hemisphere. They all have woody cones with spirally arranged scales and linear flat leaves (usually called needles) which are attached to the shoot in a variety of different ways.

a   b   c   d

The illustrations above demonstrate these differences. The leaves of Silver fir (*Abies*) leave a depressed or concave scar (**a**) while a slightly raised scar, together with a minutely stalked leaf (**b**) shows the tree is almost certainly a Douglas fir (*Pseudotsuga*). Spruces (*Picea*) are immediately notable for the prominent woody peg (*pulvinus*) that is left where the leaf (**c**) is pulled away or falls from it naturally. The leaves of pines (*Pinus*) are set in fascicles of two, three or five and bound by a basal sheath by which they are attached to the shoot (**d**). These fascicles are extensions of short or spur shoots and—despite the number of their leaves—can always be brought together to make up a simple, but divided cylinder. This adaptation probably allows the leaves to maximize their surface area for the purposes of transpiration.

The length of the shoot can also be a guide to genus; while all the family produce long shoots, some genera, namely the pines, larches (*Larix*) and cedars (*Cedrus*) also produce much shorter shoots. These grow from a bud in the axil of a needle on a long shoot, and eventually a new whorl of needles is formed. The bud in the centre of this new whorl may either be the starting point for subsequent growth or may remain dormant for years. The shorter shoots of the larches grow for several years and have many deciduous needles, a feature unique in this family.

The majority of trees in Pinaceae grow pendent cones but *Abies*, *Cedrus* and *Larix* have cones which remain erect after the female flowers have been fertilized. Those of larches ripen over one season; those of silver firs and cedars usually take longer and are further distinguished by their cones being deciduous, falling to the ground after they have opened to release their seeds. The central core of these cones, a long spike or "candle", is left standing on the shoot.

All other genera have pendent cones whose scales remain attached to their central axis and eventually fall to the ground intact.

Silver firs *Abies*

So-called because of the undersides of their foliage, most Silver firs have short leaves set in flat ranks which become more assurgent in the upper crown. Their deciduous cones develop at the top of the tree. About 40 species may be encountered.

Silver fir

Abies alba

Cone *10–15 cm, green ripening brown.* **Bracts** *pointed, reflexed.* **Leaves** *2.5 cm, with white stomata below*

Foliage *well parted on dark, pubescent shoot*

50 m. **Crown** *slender and open.* **Branches** *spreading, whorled.* **Bole** *long*

Silver fir is an important forest tree and common in the mountains of central Europe. It has thick leaves with notched tips, and non-resinous buds. King Boris fir (*A. borisii-regis*) has denser foliage, narrower leaves to 3 cm and pale-haired twigs.

Caucasian fir

Abies nordmanniana

Leaves *3 cm, tip notched, grooved, banded below*

Cone *to 15 cm.* **Bracts** *exserted*

Foliage *forward*

45 m. **Crown** *dense, conic*

This fir has a more luxuriant crown than *A. alba* and its forward-pointing foliage persists for about 6–8 years. Bornmüller fir (*A. bornmuellerana*) has longer leaves with spots of stomata by the upperside tips, shiny red-brown shoots and sticky buds.

Spanish fir

Abies pinsapo

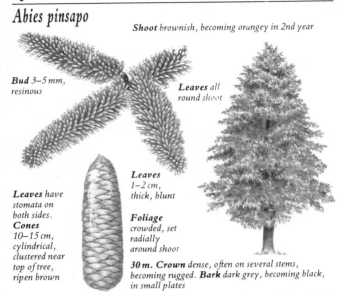

Shoot brownish, becoming orangey in 2nd year

Bud 3–5 mm, resinous

Leaves all round shoot

Leaves have stomata on both sides.
Cones 10–15 cm, cylindrical, clustered near top of tree, ripen brown

Leaves 1–2 cm, thick, blunt

Foliage crowded, set radially around shoot

30 m. Crown dense, often on several stems, becoming rugged. **Bark** dark grey, becoming black, in small plates

Spanish fir only occurs wild in southern Spain but is fairly widely planted in Europe. It is also called Hedgehog fir because of its stiff foliage; that of Algerian fir (*A. numidica*) is parted below and has a prominent band of stomata at its leaf tips.

Greek fir

Abies cephalonica

Cone to 15 cm. **Bracts** exserted, reflexed

Cones numerous on upper branches

Buds sticky

40 m. Crown conic. **Bark** fissured

Tips spiny

Leaves to 3 cm

Foliage glossy above, silvery-white below, set radially, less dense below

With a massive bole and heavy branches which sometimes rise as secondary leaders, Greek fir is often the bulkiest of the silver firs. *A. cephalonica* var. *apollonis* has denser, blunter, forward-pointing leaves, mostly arranged above the shoot.

Abies concolor ● A. concolor var. lowiana

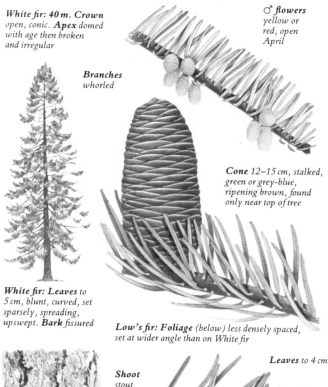

White fir: 40 m. Crown open, conic. **Apex** domed with age then broken and irregular

♂ **flowers** yellow or red, open April

Branches whorled

Cone 12–15 cm, stalked, green or grey-blue, ripening brown, found only near top of tree

White fir: Leaves to 5 cm, blunt, curved, set sparsely, spreading, upswept. **Bark** fissured

Low's fir: Foliage (below) less densely spaced, set at wider angle than on White fir

Leaves to 4 cm

Shoot stout, glabrous

Bark brown or black, often fissured orange-brown. **Shoot** pale brown or bright green, turning copper-brown or orange-brown in 2nd year

White fir grows wild in the western USA and parts of Mexico, and is recognizable by its long, assurgent, bluish leaves which smell of lemons when crushed. Low's fir, from Oregon and California, has longer leaves which either spread flat along the shoot or rise on both sides to form a wide U-shaped "groove". While it therefore combines several features of White fir, which grows to the south of its range, with several of Grand fir, which is native further north, Low's fir is ultimately distinguishable from other silver firs by the combination of lax, bluish leaves with a fissured bark usually resembling that of Douglas fir (p 49).

Grand fir

Abies grandis

Foliage *flat on shoots.* **Leaves** *5 cm.* **Buds** *2 mm, conic, grey-white, and resinous*

60 m. Crown *conic*

Cone *9 cm, tapering resinous, ripening brown*

Branches *whorled, usually level.* **Bark** *smooth, shiny when young, later cracked*

A very fast-growing species, Grand fir is an important forest tree from western North America, identified by its flat foliage which becomes more assurgent in the upper crown. West Himalayan fir (*A. pindrow*) has large globular buds and longer leaves to 9 cm, spreading down at the sides of its glabrous, ash-grey shoots.

Pacific fir

Abies amabilis

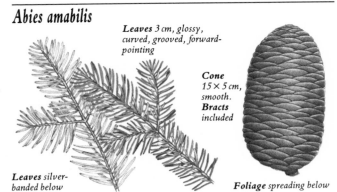

Leaves *3 cm, glossy, curved, grooved, forward-pointing*

Cone *15 × 5 cm, smooth.* **Bracts** *included*

Leaves *silver-banded below*

Foliage *spreading below*

The shapely crown and rich foliage of this fir justify its specific name which may be translated as "lovely". It is native from British Columbia to California. Maries fir (*A. mariesii*) is its closest relative and its 2 cm leaves are glossier. Its shoot has dense orange-red, not light brown, pubescence.

Noble fir

Abies procera

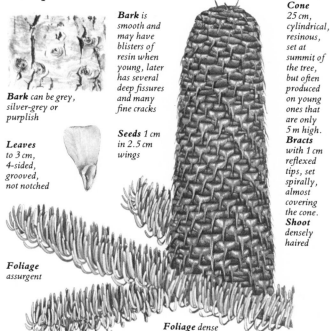

Bark can be grey, silver-grey or purplish

Bark is smooth and may have blisters of resin when young, later has several deep fissures and many fine cracks

Seeds 1 cm in 2.5 cm wings

Leaves to 3 cm, 4-sided, grooved, not notched

Foliage assurgent

Foliage dense

Cone 25 cm, cylindrical, resinous, set at summit of the tree, but often produced on young ones that are only 5 m high. **Bracts** with 1 cm reflexed tips, set spirally, almost covering the cone. **Shoot** densely haired

Noble fir is remarkable for the size of its cones which may contain up to 1,000 seeds and for its silvery fissured mature bark. Its lower branches carry many crimson male flowers in spring.

Red fir

Abies magnifica

40 m. Crown narrow, columnar-conic and symmetrical. **Branches** short and whorled, assurgent

Bark thick and corky. **Bole** stout and long, tapering

Cone to 20 × 10 cm, smooth, initially golden green, ripening purple-brown. **Bracts** included

Leaves 4 cm, lax, curved, 4-sided, ungrooved

This fir is native to Oregon and California and while closely related to Noble fir, has ungrooved, longer and less densely set foliage. Its name comes from the red bark of mature trees. The cones of Shasta fir (*A. magnifica* var. *shastensis*) have exserted bracts.

Veitch fir

Abies veitchii

Cone *8 cm, cylindrical, flat-topped, purple-blue initially, ripens brown, smoothly wrinkled.* **Bracts** *slightly exserted*

Foliage *all pointing forwards, spreading below, rising at 45° to shoot above*

Bud *3 mm, shiny, red-purple*

Bark *dark grey-green, with white patches on old trees*

Leaves *3 cm, grey-green above, silver-white below, square-tipped*

Shoot *slightly ribbed, has brown hairs with young.* **Foliage** *set densely*

Veitch firs form trees to 20 m with tapered, flat-topped crowns. On trees whose crowns reach the ground the lowest branches are very upswept revealing the silver underside of their foliage. It is a native of Japan, as is Sakhalin fir (*A. sachalinensis*), with longer, narrower, bright green leaves to 3.5 cm.

Korean fir

Abies koreana

15 m. Crown *conic with slightly ascending branches.* **Leaves** *spreading below shoot, curving upwards above*

Leaves *1–1.5 cm, glossy green or yellow-green above, tips often white*

Bark *shiny, dark brown to black, smooth, spotted conspicuously with lenticels.* **Leaves** *vividly white underneath, rather radial and spaced along shoot*

Shoot *fawn.* **Buds** *small, globular, initially pale brown but soon covered with white resin*

Cone *7 cm, pointed, purple, ripening brown.* **Bracts** *reflexed, very exserted*

This silver fir, first discovered in 1907 on an island off Korea, usually only manages to grow to 10 m in 40 years. It is very free in producing its small violet cones, often as a young tree less than 1 m tall. The strongly exserted and reflexed bracts show clearly how cone scales in the Pine family are radially arranged.

Abies forrestii var. *forrestii* • *A. forrestii* var. *smithii*

Forrest fir cone (right) is 7–12 cm long, cylindrical or barrel-shaped, top dimpled, violet, ripening brown over winter. **Bracts** exserted, often reflexed with very prominent awl-like cusps to 5 mm

Smith fir cone (right) often larger, occasionally to 15 cm. **Bracts** exserted, with cusps up to 1 cm, pointing upright except near base of cone. **Bract edges** well exposed, bright blue-purple with light brown edges

Forrest fir shoot (below) stout, red-brown, usually glabrous and finely roughened; in second year deeper colour with pale fissures. **Foliage** may be radial

Smith fir shoot (above) brownish orange, with a dense, short pubescence of the same colour. **Leaves** close more over top of shoot. **Foliage** short, perpendicular

Smith fir leaves (left) shorter, to 2.5 cm, off-white below, grey bloomed above

Forrest foliage (left) to 4 cm, spreading around shoot, often lax below, dense and may be parted. **Leaf** green above, white below

These two firs were discovered in China and introduced into Britain by George Forrest, after whom they are named. Smith fir is chiefly distinguished by its densely pubescent shoots and longer cusps, and although both trees grow to 25m, Smith fir has a more columnar and denser crown than Forrest fir. Related species from the Himalayas and west China include Himalayan fir (*A. spectabilis*), which has ash-grey or light brown shoots pubescent in deep grooves and Delavay fir (*A. delavayi*), which has bright violet narrow cones, maroon shoots, orange buds, and inrolled leaf margins which make the leaves narrow and square-tipped. Farges fir (*A. fargesii*) has stout 2.5 cm needles on glossy, purple shoots and conic, purple buds.

47

Nikko fir

Abies homolepis

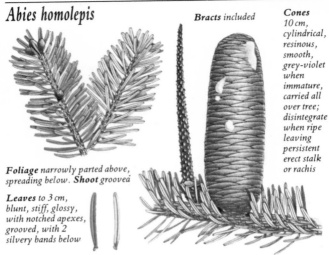

Bracts *included*

Cones 10 cm, cylindrical, resinous, smooth, grey-violet when immature, carried all over tree; disintegrate when ripe leaving persistent erect stalk or rachis

Foliage *narrowly parted above, spreading below.* **Shoot** *grooved*

Leaves *to 3 cm, blunt, stiff, glossy, with notched apexes, grooved, with 2 silvery bands below*

Nikko fir, tolerant of urban pollution, has strongly ridged and grooved glabrous shoots. Min fir (*A. recurvata*) has smooth shoots, more ovoid, 8 cm cones, and bluntly pointed needles, green on both surfaces, that may point backwards.

Santa Lucia fir

Abies bracteata

Foliage *parted, forward-pointing, widely spaced.* **Shoot** *stout, glabrous, almost shiny, green-purple to dark brown*

Cones *8 cm, ovoid, uncommon.* **Bracts** *remarkable for erect or spreading cusps that reach 3 cm, and often carry large blobs of resin.* **Bud** *to 2 cm, spindle-shaped, very sharply pointed, not resinous, pale brown*

Leaves *to 5 cm, leathery, hard, very sharp spiny tips, persist for up to 5 years, and closely resemble those of California nutmeg (see p 22)*

Leaves *white-banded below*

Unique in its cones, its beech-like buds and its foliage, this silver fir grows wild in the Santa Lucia mountains of California. Manchurian fir (*A. holophylla*) has similar assurgent foliage but ovoid-conic, resinous buds.

Douglas fir

Pseudotsuga menziesii

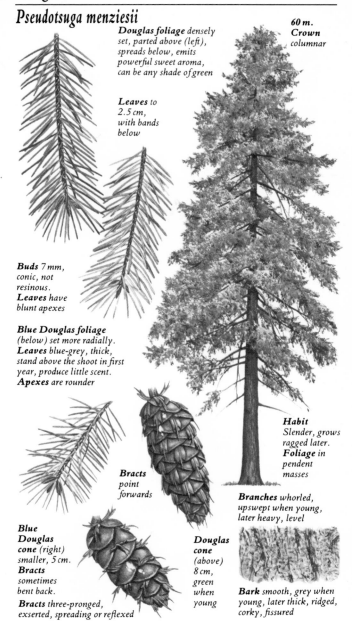

Douglas foliage densely set, parted above (left), spreads below, emits powerful sweet aroma, can be any shade of green

Leaves to 2.5 cm, with bands below

60 m. Crown columnar

Buds 7 mm, conic, not resinous. **Leaves** have blunt apexes

Blue Douglas foliage (below) set more radially. **Leaves** blue-grey, thick, stand above the shoot in first year, produce little scent. **Apexes** are rounder

Bracts point forwards

Habit Slender, grows ragged later. **Foliage** in pendent masses

Branches whorled, upswept when young, later heavy, level

Blue Douglas cone (right) smaller, 5 cm. **Bracts** sometimes bent back.

Bracts three-pronged, exserted, spreading or reflexed

Douglas cone (above) 8 cm, green when young

Bark smooth, grey when young, later thick, ridged, corky, fissured

The genus *Pseudotsuga* was named after its resemblance to the Hemlocks (pp 58–9) but it also shows an affinity with *Abies* (pp 41–8). Douglas fir, its main species, is native to the western side of the American Rockies and has been widely replanted for its vigorous growth and the excellence of its timber. Blue Douglas fir is smaller and slower growing. It differs in its cones and its blunt foliage, and grows wild in the drier eastern Rockies between Montana and Mexico.

49

True Cedars *Cedrus*

True cedars develop two types of foliage and have deciduous cones which ripen over two years and disintegrate *in situ* to release triangular-winged seeds. "Atlas—ascending, Deodar—drooping, Lebanon—level" can be useful mnemonic for identifying cedars by their *growing* branch tips.

Cedar of Lebanon

Cedrus libani

40 m. Crown broad, flat-topped. Large, horizontal layers of dense foliage

Bark grey-brown, fissured; smooth, dark grey on young trees

Branches massive, arching then level. **Bole** huge

Foliage dense, darkest green of cedars. Can be grey or glaucous. **Buds** 2–3 mm, brown, ovoid. **Shoots** brown, pubescent

Cone from 8–14 cm. Apex sometimes depressed. Resinous

Leaves narrow. Taper to sharp, translucent tips. On young, long shoots: 2 cm, set singly and spirally; on older 2–3 mm spur-shoots: 3 cm, in whorls of 10–20

Cedar of Lebanon grows naturally in Asia Minor and has become a familiar ornamental in parks and at stately homes. Cyprus cedar (*C. brevifolia*) is less common and has shorter leaves, narrower, more ovoid cones and a more conical crown.

Atlas cedar
Cedrus atlantica

Cone *8 cm, usually depressed*

♂ **flowers** *reach 5 cm by Sept when pollen is shed and dispersed by wind*

40 m. Crown *broad, conic.* **Branches** *widely spaced.* **Leaves** *2.5 cm on long shoots; 2 cm, in whorls of 30–45 on 1–2 cm spur-shoots.* **Buds** *ovoid, 2–3 cm*

Native to the mountains of north Africa, wild Atlas cedars are found in both green and glaucous forms. The very blue 'Glauca' clone shown here is the one most commonly encountered as an ornamental and derives its colour from the wax coating its leaves.

Deodar

Cedrus deodara

40 m. Crown *broad, columnar, conic.* **Leader** *and long shoots always droop.* **Stem** *single. Young trees blue-grey*

Cone *10 cm broad, egg-shaped, ripening dark brown*

Foliage *dark green, bright green when new.* **Leaves** *5 cm on long shs, 3.5 cm on short shs.* **Buds** *only 1 mm*

In the western Himalayas where they grow wild, Deodars can reach 70 m. Pendulous branchlets on spreading and slightly downswept branches are their most distinctive features.

Larch *Larix*

Some leaves of these deciduous conifers are set singly on long shoots, but most foliage is set in whorls on short spur-like shoots. The small, erect, persistent cones and the short and long shoots are the key identifying features.

European larch • Hybrid larch

Larix decidua • *Larix eurolepis*

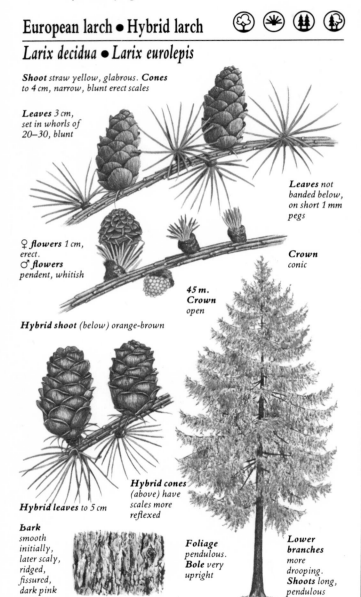

Shoot straw yellow, glabrous. **Cones** to 4 cm, narrow, blunt erect scales

Leaves 3 cm, set in whorls of 20–30, blunt

Leaves not banded below, on short 1 mm pegs

♀ **flowers** 1 cm, erect.
♂ **flowers** pendent, whitish

Crown conic

45 m. Crown open

Hybrid shoot (below) orange-brown

Hybrid leaves to 5 cm

Hybrid cones (above) have scales more reflexed

Bark smooth initially, later scaly, ridged, fissured, dark pink

Foliage pendulous. **Bole** very upright

Lower branches more drooping. **Shoots** long, pendulous

Native to the mountains of northern and central Europe, European larch is the only European conifer to shed all its leaves annually. Hybrid, or Dunkeld, larch is a natural cross between European and Japanese larch, identifiable by shoots and cones, and is more widely planted for its better form, greater disease resistance and faster growth.

Japanese larch

Larix kaempferi

Cone 3 cm, ovoid, has very reflexed scales. **Bracts** hidden

Shoot identifiable by small 5 mm 'knobs'

Leaves 4 cm, broad, with 2 wide grey bands below. **Foliage** very densely set

Bark scaly

45 m. Crown broad

This species, native to Mount Fuji, is more vigorous than European larch and forms a shorter, stouter tree with heavier branches. It can be distinguished by its purplish-red shoots, wider leaves and squatter cones with scales reflexed like rose petals.

Tamarack

Larix laricina

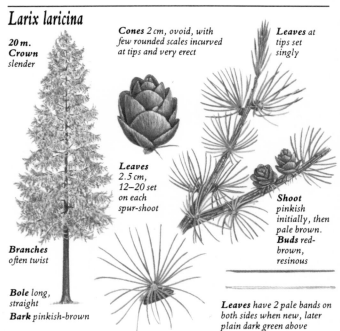

20 m. Crown slender

Cones 2 cm, ovoid, with few rounded scales incurved at tips and very erect

Leaves at tips set singly

Leaves 2.5 cm, 12–20 set on each spur-shoot

Shoot pinkish initially, then pale brown. **Buds** red-brown, resinous

Branches often twist

Bole long, straight
Bark pinkish-brown

Leaves have 2 pale bands on both sides when new, later plain dark green above

Tamarack is the most widely distributed conifer in North America growing across Canada from Alaska to the Atlantic, and as far south as Pennsylvania in the USA, in anything from swamps to sub-Arctic conditions. Dahurian larch (*L. gmelinii*) has a gaunt crown and smaller leaves.

Spruces *Picea*

Spruces have single pointed needles which are set on a *pulvinus*, an extension of the shoot. When the needles fall they leave behind a short peg, making the bare shoots prickly.

Norway spruce

Picea abies

Cones *pendulous*

Buds *5 mm, non-resinous, ovoid-conic*

Needles *4-sided, 2 cm.*
Shoot *yellow or orange-brown*

Cone *to 18 cm, cylindrical.*
Scale tips *rounded or rhomboid*

Cones *only in top whorls*

Bark *reddish or coppery brown, with small papery scales, purplish in old trees, smooth, cracked*

Norway spruce, the familiar "Christmas tree", native to central and northern Europe, has longer needles and longer, less woody cones than Siberian spruce (*P. obovata*), from northern Eurasia, and Wilson spruce (*P. wilsonia*) which also has ash grey shoots.

Caucasian spruce

Picea orientalis

Needles *very short, 8 mm, squarish, rounded at tips, shiny dark green, parted below*

Shoots *of young trees long, twisted; in old trees straight, projecting from crown*

35 m. Crown *narrow conic*

Shoot *whitish-brown, densely hairy.*
Buds *4 mm, with red tips to basal scales*

Crown *open when young, dense when old.*
Bark *grey, smooth, pinkish with age*

Caucasian spruce is unique in its short needles, and has spindle-shaped, often curved cones that grow to 7 cm. Likiang spruce (*P. likiangensis*) has buff shoots, blue-grey needles and papery purple cones to 15 cm.

Serbian spruce

Picea omorika

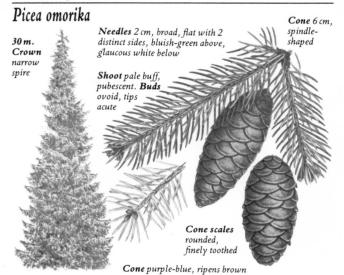

Cone 6 cm, spindle-shaped

Needles 2 cm, broad, flat with 2 distinct sides, bluish-green above, glaucous white below

30 m. Crown narrow spire

Shoot pale buff, pubescent. **Buds** ovoid, tips acute

Cone scales rounded, finely toothed

Cone purple-blue, ripens brown

Native to a single Yugoslavian river valley but widely planted throughout Europe, this spruce owes its spire-like habit not to the branches being short, but to their lying recumbent down the stem before curving out, an adaptation to prevent snow damage.

Sitka spruce

Picea sitchensis

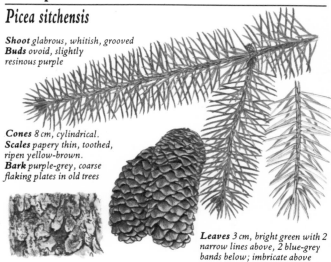

Shoot glabrous, whitish, grooved
Buds ovoid, slightly resinous purple

Cones 8 cm, cylindrical.
Scales papery thin, toothed, ripen yellow-brown.
Bark purple-grey, coarse flaking plates in old trees

Leaves 3 cm, bright green with 2 narrow lines above, 2 blue-grey bands below; imbricate above

Sitka spruce is native along the west coast of North America, where it can grow to 80 m. It is widely planted for timber in western Britain. Jezo spruce (*P. jezoensis*), from north-eastern Asia, has denser, assurgent blunt leathery needles to 1.5 cm, and a gaunt habit. Sargent spruce (*P. brachytyla*), from western China, has leaves to 1.5 cm which are silvery white below and curve down at the sides. Its 13 cm cones are conical.

White spruce

Picea glauca

Crushed foliage *very odorous*

Buds
*5 mm,
ovoid,
smooth,
shiny pale
brown*

Cone *6 cm,
ovoid.* **Scales**
*smooth,
round, thin
but woody*

Foliage *assurgent, all
above shoot.* **Needles**
*even length, 1.5 cm,
round, grey or blue-grey
with narrow white bands*

Shoot *glabrous, white,
later orange-brown*

White spruce, which has a wide range across Canada and northern USA, grows to 20 m with a narrow conic crown. Engelmann spruce (*P. engelmannii*) differs in its longer, softer, 2.5 cm needles, hairy shoots and papery scales. Black spruce (*P. mariana*) has 2 cm 4-angled spreading leaves.

Colorado blue spruce

Picea pungens 'Glauca'

**25 m.
Crown**
*columnar-
conic,
dense*

Needles *2 cm, arranged
radially but upswept below;
4-sided, stiff, sharp.*
Buds *1 cm, with long
slender scales at base*

Cone *12 cm,
cylindrical.* **Scales**
thin, papery.
Margins *wavy*

Branches *level, later pendent with tips upswept.*
Bark *thick, purplish-brown, coarse and flaking*

This form of the normally grey-green foliaged Colorado spruce is the one usually cultivated. Dragon spruce (*P. asperata*) has grey exfoliating papery bark and lacks a ring of scales at the base of the bud; its cones have round woody scales. Tigertail spruce (*P. polita*) has viciously sharp shiny dark green radial leaves and cones with rounded scales.

Brewer spruce

Picea breweriana

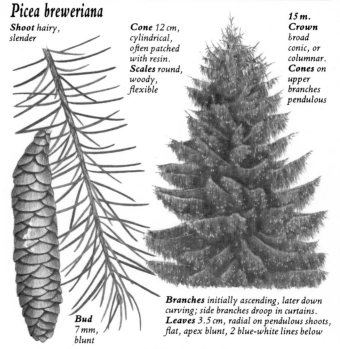

Shoot hairy, slender

Cone 12 cm, cylindrical, often patched with resin. **Scales** round, woody, flexible

15 m.
Crown broad conic, or columnar.
Cones on upper branches pendulous

Bud 7 mm, blunt

Branches initially ascending, later down curving; side branches droop in curtains.
Leaves 3.5 cm, radial on pendulous shoots, flat, apex blunt, 2 blue-white lines below

A native of Oregon and California, this fine weeping tree has branchlets drooping vertically either side of the main branches. Sikkim spruce (*P. spinulosa*) has white glabrous shoots on an open, less pendent crown, and its leaves are not so flat.

Morinda spruce

Picea smithiana

40 m.
Crown columnar

Cone 15 cm, green, ripens brown. **Scales** thick, woody, shiny

Bud 8 mm, ovoid, shiny

Shoot shiny, cream, grooved, with shallow folds

Branches level, spaced.
Branchlets pendent. **Bark** hard

Foliage radial, spaced.
Needle 4 cm, round

Morinda spruce is native from Afghanistan to Nepal, and has the largest cones of the genus, up to 20 × 5 cm, borne throughout the upper crown. Schrenk spruce (*P. schrenkiana*) is similar, but has less weeping branchlets, grey-green leaves less radially arranged and long pale buds.

Hemlocks *Tsuga*

Hemlocks are a small group of conifers differing from spruces in their flattened needles, usually notched at apex, and the slender branchlets which lack the prominent *pulvini* of the *Picea*. Except in the Mountain hemlock, the cones are less than 3.5 cm.

Western hemlock

Tsuga heterophylla

Cone *3 cm, pendulous, ovoid, scales rounded, entire*

Needles *2 cm at side but only 1 cm above, tip rounded*

Shoots *slender, ribbed, cream-brown, hairs brown.*
Buds *small, ovoid, non-resinous*

Leaf *has white bands below*

50 m. Crown *conic, broader on old trees, dense, pendulous tips to straight branches ascending at 45°, low branches droop*

Young tree *(right) has leading shoot which arches over*

Foliage *spreading below, parted above*

Bark *thin, smooth, fissured and ridged in older trees.* **Bole** *straight, fluted; single stem straight from ground to tip of tree*

Western hemlock, a native of the western half of North America, is a fast-growing tree with attractive foliage, extremely tolerant of shade condition. The specific name refers to the irregular foliage arrangement, also a feature of *T. diversifolia*, a Japanese species, which has entire leaf margins, shorter leaves that are vividly white below and orange shoots.

Eastern hemlock

Tsuga canadensis

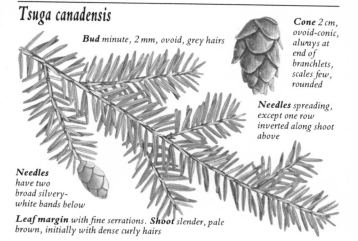

Bud *minute, 2 mm, ovoid, grey hairs*

Cone *2 cm, ovoid-conic, always at end of branchlets, scales few, rounded*

Needles *spreading, except one row inverted along shoot above*

Needles *have two broad silvery-white bands below*

Leaf margin *with fine serrations.* **Shoot** *slender, pale brown, initially with dense curly hairs*

Unlike *heterophylla* Eastern hemlock grows on a multiple stem and grows in the eastern half of North America. Carolina hemlock (*T. carolinensis*), from the south-eastern USA, has entire margined needles on shiny orange shoots, and larger long–ovoid cones to 3.5 cm with thin rounded scales.

Mountain hemlock

Tsuga mertensiana

Needles *2.5 cm, slender, stomata on both sides*

Leaves *dense, green or grey*

Leaves *set all around shoot.*
Shoot *hairy, shiny, pale brown.*
Bark *deeply furrowed with rounded ridges, rough on younger trees and more orangey*

30 m. Crown *spire-like, tip nodding*

Cone *8 cm, cylindrical, tapers at both ends, scales rounded, reflexed when cone open*

Mountain hemlock is midway between a *Tsuga* and a *Picea*, but is distinguishable by the petiole-like base of its needle. It is used for timber, and has a similar though higher distribution to Western hemlock, with which it has hybridized to produce Jeffrey hemlock (*T. x jeffreyi*) with spreading partly radial needles.

Pines *Pinus*

The members of this genus can be identified by their leaf groupings and divide into hard pines (Diploxylin) such as Scots pine (p 60) and soft pines (Hapsloxylin) like Blue pine (p 67). The former have leaves in fascicles of two or three, rough bark and cones whose woody scales have central umbos; the latter have leaves in fives and softer cones with umbos at their scale tips.

Scots pine

Pinus sylvestris

35 m. Crown *rounded on old trees, conical when young.* **Branches** *short, horizontal or slightly ascending*

Buds *resinous, short-pointed, cylindrical*

Cone *8 cm, ovoid, green in 1st year.* **Scales** *not spined.* **Bark** *in upper crown orange, flaking, heavily fissured at base*

Shoot *glabrous, ridged*

Leaves *8 cm (15 cm on young trees), broad, stout, twisted*

This tree has a wide natural range across Europe and Asia from the Atlantic to Pacific. Its change in bark colour and texture is distinctive, as is its grey-green to bright blue-green foliage; that of 'Aurea' is golden in winter. Aleppo pine (*P. halepensis*) has sparser, shiny green leaves, red-brown buds and grey shoots. Its shiny red cones often remain closed on the tree.

Pinus nigra var. *nigra* • *P. nigra* var. *maritima*

Foliage dense, in forward-pointing bunches. **Shoot** ridged and shiny

Leaves 15 cm, stiff, curved in 2nd year. **Sheaths** 1 cm, persistent

Buds long, 12 mm

Bark coarse, deeply furrowed. **Corsican pine** (below): **45 m.** **Crown** lighter

Cones (both trees) 8 cm

Corsican foliage slender, spreading, twisted

Leaves 18 cm, in spaced fascicles. **Bud** resinous

Widely distributed throughout the Mediterranean, Black pine (*P. nigra*) occurs in several forms, two of which are shown here: Austrian pine is a hardy, densely crowned tree, usually growing on several stems to 30 m, Corsican pine is more vigorous and often planted for its timber. Their cones are identical but they can usually be identified by their shoots, buds and leaves. Bosnian pine (*P. leucodermis*) has similarly dense foliage but cobalt blue unripe cones and bloomed shoots.

61

Shore pine • Lodgepole pine

Pinus contorta var. *contorta* • *P. contorta* var. *latifolia*

Shore pine leaves 5 cm, straight.
Lodgepole leaves to 10 cm

Shore pine foliage dense

Lodgepole crown more open. **Bark** finely scaled

Cones (both trees) 5 cm, prickled

Lodgepole foliage less dense, splayed, twisted

♂ **flowers** at base of new shoots shedding pollen in April

30 m

Extensively planted in European forests, these trees can be distinguished by their foliage. Jack pine (*P. banksiana*) has shorter, 4 cm leaves and curved, forward-pointing cones.

Stone pine

Pinus pinea

20 m. Crown wide

Leaves long, 14 cm

Cone 10 cm, large, glossy, ripening over 3 years. **Scales** smooth. **Umbo** "rings" show 2 years' growth

Branches radiate from short bole. **Foliage** sparse. **Bark** very fissured

Instantly recognizable by its umbrella-shaped crown, this Mediterranean species has large, 2 cm, wingless seeds which have been a culinary delicacy since the time of the Romans.

Maritime pine

Pinus pinaster

Umbos *upcurved*

Bark *deeply fissured*

Bud *2 cm, with scales at tips recurved*

Cone *to 20 cm, often clustered and persisting unopened*

Leaves *very long, to 25 cm, stout with rough margins*

This tree thrives on poor, sandy sites and is widely planted in Mediterranean countries for its resin. This is tapped by longitudinal wounds made in the bark and is used in turpentine manufacture. Its leaves are the longest and stoutest of any European pine.

Monterey pine

Pinus radiata

Leaves *long, 15 cm, slender, soft, shiny*

40 m. Crown *large, domed, high, appears black from a distance.* **Branches** *heavy, spread widely*

Bole *long*

Leaves *set densely in 3s.* **Shoot** *glabrous.* **Cone** *large, 12 cm, ovoid, extremely persistent.* **Umbos** *rounded*

Native to California, this tree has been widely planted for its timber. Its obliquely based cones may persist for over twenty years and often require the heat of forest fires to open them.

Ponderosa pine

Pinus ponderosa

40 m. **Crown** variable

Leaves to 22 cm

Crown fairly open. **Bole** long, straight

Leaves dense, stout, usually in fascicles of 3. **Sheath** 2 cm

Cone 12 cm, when falls base left behind. **Scales** ridged, prickled

This tree grows at varying altitudes and on dry sites throughout western North America. Its foliage is very variable—even on the same tree, leaves may be set in fascicles of both two and three.

Jeffrey pine

Pinus jeffreyi

Foliage dense, persisting 5–8 years

Cone 18 cm, deltoid when open

Umbos recurved

Shoot bloomed blue-grey

Bud 3 cm, pointed. **Scale tips** free, non-resinous

Leaves 25 cm, stiff, spreading, bluish-green or grey

Native to Oregon and California and rarely exceeding 35 m, Jeffrey pine is smaller than Ponderosa but can grow at greater heights. Its distinguishing features are its bloomed shoot, and when available, its larger, broad-based cones.

Coulter pine

Pinus coulterii

Cone *huge, 35 cm, weighs up to 2.5 kg.*
Seeds *12 mm.* **Scales** *thick.*
Umbos *sharp*

Foliage *stout, rigid, spaced, not densely set, becomes crinkled in 2nd year*

Shoot *stout, glabrous*

Leaves *30 cm.* **Sheath** *2.5 cm*

While closely related to Ponderosa and Jeffrey pines, Coulter pine can be recognized by the size of its cones, normally set at the summit, or its longer hanging leaves. Digger pine (*P. sabiniana*) holds its 25 cm leaves level.

Lacebark pine

Pinus bungeana

Foliage *spaced, not set densely on shoot*

Bark *smooth, flaking through white, yellow, olive and purple to grey-green*

Leaves *8 cm, slender, smooth, finely toothed, in close fascicles.* **Sheath** *deciduous*

Cone *6 cm, on 2 cm stalk.* **Umbos** *dorsal, spined*

This species has a low, usually bushy crown and is cultivated for the splendour of its bark. This is initially smooth and grey-green and then flakes away to leave rounded white patches which turn through yellow, green, red and purple to purple-brown. In its native China, the bark of old trees turns a further chalk white.

Arolla pine

Pinus cembra

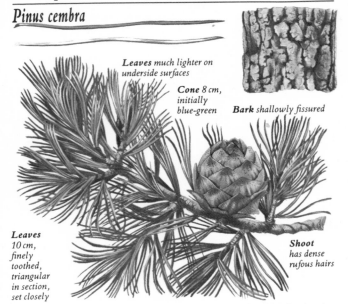

Leaves much lighter on underside surfaces

Cone 8 cm, initially blue-green

Bark shallowly fissured

Leaves 10 cm, finely toothed, triangular in section, set closely

Shoot has dense rufous hairs

Arolla, or Swiss stone pine, grows wild at high altitudes in the mountains of central Europe, while in parts of Scandinavia it is planted for its timber. Its contrasting leaves and broad, dense crown reaching 25 m are distinctive. The large seeds are edible.

Macedonian pine

Pinus peuce

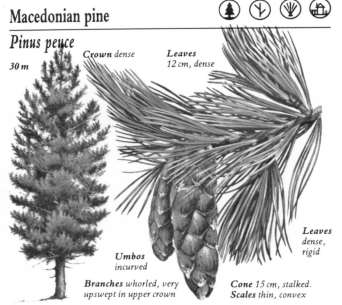

30 m

Crown dense

Leaves 12 cm, dense

Leaves dense, rigid

Umbos incurved

Branches whorled, very upswept in upper crown

Cone 15 cm, stalked. **Scales** thin, convex

Rarely planted for timber outside its native Albania, Bulgaria and Yugoslavia, this attractive tree is similar to Blue pine but has finer shoots, more curved cones and leaves which are shorter, denser, rigid and more forward-pointing.

Blue pine

Pinus wallachiana

Leaves 20 cm, pendulous, green on outer surfaces

Leaf margins finely toothed

Bark smooth in upper crown

Cones 15–30 cm, 10 cm wide when open, resinous, initially blue-green

Scales incurved except at base. **Cone stalk** 4 cm

Blue pine, often known as Bhutan pine, is indigenous throughout the Himalayas. It has been widely planted as an ornamental and forms a broad, heavily branched tree to 35 m, with stout, glabrous shoots and curved leaves. Mexican white pine (*P. ayacahuite*) has straight needles and more tapered cones.

Armand pine

Pinus armandii

Leaves droop, usually straight, set at shoot ends

Leaves 16 cm, sparse. **Shoot base** bare

Cone stalk stout, 3 cm

Cone 15 cm, erect before ripening. **Scales** thick. **Bark** smooth at first

Dedicated to its discoverer, Père Armand David, this pine has a very wide distribution across China and in Burma. It resembles Blue pine but has finer shoots and barrel-shaped cones.

Japanese white pine

Pinus parvifolia

Foliage
blue-green
on outer
surface,
silvery
glaucous
on inner

Leaves
5–8 cm,
slender,
twisted,
blunt, set
together in
1st year,
splaying
out later.
Margins
very finely
toothed.
Sheath
1 cm

Cones 5 cm,
egg-shaped,
almost
sessile

Umbos
slender and
terminal.
Seeds 1 cm

In its wild form, this species grows to a height of 25 m but is more usually encountered as a lower, slow-growing tree that rarely reaches 10 m. It has a wide crown and tiered branches and was probably developed for Japanese ornamental gardens. The leaves of both types are the most twisting of any pine.

Western white pine

Pinus monticola

Cones 35 cm, tapering, slightly curved,
set on short stalks, numerous.
Scales thin, rounded, resinous

Foliage dense,
set in tufts

Leaves 10 cm, stiff, straight, rough,
persistent, inner surfaces lighter.
Margins rough

Shoot
slender with
dense coppery hairs

Native to the Pacific coast of North America and as far inland as Montana, *P. monticola* has a dense crown and can reach heights of 50 m. Like all soft pines, the bark of young trees and that high up on old trees is smooth and grey-green and often attacked by blister rust, a fungal disease which affects all American white pines and kills many old trees.

Weymouth pine

Pinus strobus

Leaves *12 cm, paler on inner surfaces*

Shoot *ridged behind leaves, only hairy on ridges*

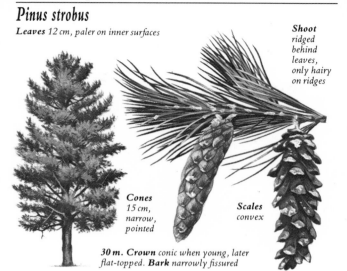

Cones *15 cm, narrow, pointed*

Scales *convex*

30 m. Crown *conic when young, later flat-topped.* **Bark** *narrowly fissured*

Native to the forests of eastern North America, Weymouth pine forms a tree to 40 m, often on several stems, and differs from Western white pine in its glabrous shoots and shorter, pointed cones which are only 15 cm high. The leaves are stiffer and only persist for two seasons. Susceptible to white pine blister rust.

Bristlecone pine

Pinus aristata

Cone *8 cm, spreading, with short stalk.* **Umbo** *has 6 mm spreading or curving prickle*

Bud *7 mm, pointed, scales free at base*

Foliage *very dense, persistent, curving forwards on stout orange shoot*

Leaves *4 cm, thick and stiff, dotted with resin spots.* **Margins** *entire*

The most common of the species from south-western USA which are known as "foxtail" pines because of their long, dense foliage, Bristlecone pine has leaves which persist for up to 15 years. Balfour pine (*P. balfouriana*) survives at high altitudes and has longer, unspotted leaves and cones with less prominent spines.

The broadleaf trees

Leaf palmately lobed and veined in uniform pattern

Veins may be either impressed (below surface of leaf) or prominent (striking or raised above surface of leaf)

Palmate venation and lobulation originates from petiole

Serrated margin, fits venation pattern

Petiole enables leaf to twist round to follow the light

The trees known as the broadleaf trees, because their leaves have broad blades, are more properly classified as the Angiospermae, so called because their seeds develop from ovules which are enclosed in an ovary. All but two can also be classified as Dicotyledonae, because their seedlings have two seed leaves, and all are hardwoods, as they produce hard timber.

The shape of the leaf, the best feature for identification purposes, is governed by its composition and function, a vital element being the venation system, illustrated above in a sycamore leaf. The veins strengthen the thin blade, and the many complex patterns they form are useful for identification. Their main function, however, and that of the leaf, is to produce energy for the tree by photosynthesis—the fixing (i.e., turning into solid form) of carbon from the air. This process has to take place in daylight and needs water, which is transported up from the root system to spread across the surface of the leaf blade through the network of veins. The veins are two-way channels; they transport water and nutrients to the leaf, and carry the sugar sap, the end product of photosynthesis, to the rest of the tree.

After assisting in photosynthesis, the water from the roots transpires or evaporates into the atmosphere, something which happens to a far lesser extent in most conifers because the thick waxy surface of their thin needles retains moisture. Temperate broadleaf trees are nearly all deciduous, dropping all their leaves each winter. Once the temperature drops, the tree cannot extract from the cold soil enough water to maintain transpiration, and freezing temperatures would damage the leaves. The nutrient material is withdrawn from the leaves before they wither and die, and they then fall, leaving a scar behind where they grew from the shoot. The leaves decay on the ground to form a rich mould.

Flowers

The broadleaf trees flower for a relatively short time, but these flowers are very useful in identification. While conifers transfer the pollen from the male to the female flowers on the wind, most broadleaves are insect pollinated, and their flowers have brightly coloured petals and strong scents to attract the insects. Four types of flower arrangement are illustrated above. A **raceme (a)** is a simple group of stalked flowers on a long single rachis. A **panicle (b)** is a looser compound or branched flower cluster. An **umbel (c)** is an inflorescence with pedicels all rising from the same point. A **corymb (d)** is a flat-topped flower cluster in which the outside flowers open first.

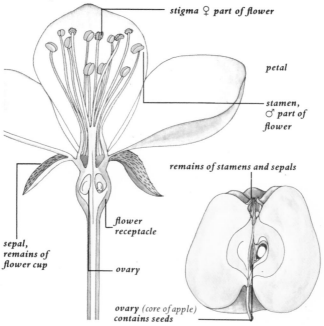

stigma ♀ part of flower

petal

stamen, ♂ part of flower

remains of stamens and sepals

flower receptacle

sepal, remains of flower cup

ovary

ovary (core of apple) contains seeds

One mode of the transition from flower to fruit is illustrated with the apple above. The flesh develops from the flower receptacle, and once the petals have dropped, the stamens and sepals wither until their remains are at the base of the fruit. What was the ovary becomes the core of the apple, which contains the seeds.

71

Fruit

The basic function of the fruit is to protect the seeds as they develop, until they are ready for dispersal to propagate the species. The fruit may be sparser than the flowers, either because some of the flowers did not develop or because the majority of the inflorescence was male. There are several different types of fruit: the apple illustrated on the previous page is a **pome**, which has a fleshy covering around one or more seeds in several fused cells; and some other examples are illustrated below. A **capsule (a)**, as borne by eucalyptus trees, is a hard woody pod which releases many small seeds through 3–6 terminal seeds. A **drupe (b)**, such as a cherry for example, has a fleshy exterior around a stone which contains one or more seeds. A **cone-like structure (c)**, as borne by the alders, has spirally or oppositely arranged scales which each carry two or more seeds. A **samara (d)**, as borne by ashes, has a single seed in a case on the end of a long wing. A **nut (e)**, such as the acorn, bears its seeds inside a hard shell; the acorn is set in a cup called an **involucre** or **cupule**.

Seed germination

The few seeds which alight on suitable ground can lie dormant for one or two years before germination. They are gradually softened by moisture from the soil, and eventually a tiny root is produced by cell division, which breaks through the seed coat and penetrates the ground. It next develops tiny hairs to extract water and nutrients from the earth; these are renewed every year throughout its life. Sometimes two seed leaves withdraw from the withered seed casing as the seedling, the first plant, is formed. In the Horse chestnut, illustrated below, they remain inside.

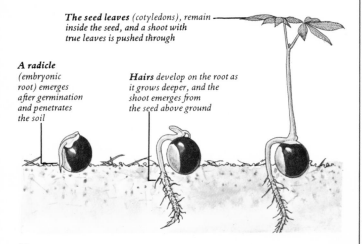

The seed leaves (cotyledons), remain inside the seed, and a shoot with true leaves is pushed through

A radicle (embryonic root) emerges after germination and penetrates the soil

Hairs develop on the root as it grows deeper, and the shoot emerges from the seed above ground

Willow family Salicaceae

This family has 350 or so species of willow and poplar which are mainly natives of the northern hemisphere. The chief feature uniting them all is their flowers. These have neither petals nor sepals and are borne in catkins which usually appear with or before their tree's new leaves and are either male or female. Only one type is usually carried. Both willows and poplars prefer moist sites and hybridize so easily that positive identification is not always easy.

Poplars *Populus*

Poplars have wind-pollinated catkins and leaves whose broad blades have long petioles which may be flattened at one end. Their deciduous shoots bear terminal buds and all their buds have overlapping scales. Trees which have hybridized grow more vigorously and provide better timber than their parents.

White poplar

Populus alba

Shoot *slender, cottony, green in first year.* **Buds** *ovoid.* ♂ *catkin 4–8 cm, appears March, before leaves*

Blade *woolly both above and below when opens*

25 m. **Crown** *often leans.* **Branches** *twist, drooping at tips.* **Bark** *smooth cream-grey with black, rhomboid lenticels.* **Bole** *surrounded by suckers.*

Leaf *pubescence only retained below and on petiole; new midsummer leaves open snow white*

Leaves *variable, 9 cm, 5-lobed on strong shoots, 5 cm, rounded on weak shoots.* **Petiole** *4 cm, flattened*

White poplar is native to central and southern Europe, North Africa and central Asia and, with Aspen (p 74), belongs to a group of poplars with smooth barks and lobed or coarsely serrate leaves. 'Pyramidis' is a fastigiate clone, broader than Lombardy poplar (p 75); 'Richardii' has golden yellow leaves.

Grey poplar

Populus canescens

Leaves to 10 cm, orbicular or shallowly lobed, opening pubescent and snow-white, becoming glossy above, greyish below

Margins translucent

Bark smooth, ridged at base of old trees

Petiole long, 5 cm, flattened, pubescent

This natural hybrid of White poplar (p73) and Aspen reaches a height of some 35 m on a few large and heavy, arching branches. Its leaves are closer to those of the former species but their undersides are greyer and less downy; they differ from those of Aspen in being persistently pubescent below. Female Grey poplars are rare and suckering is the usual form of regeneration.

Aspen

Populus tremula

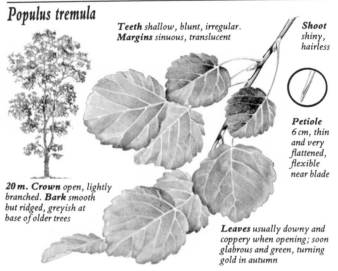

Teeth shallow, blunt, irregular. **Margins** sinuous, translucent

Shoot shiny, hairless

Petiole 6 cm, thin and very flattened, flexible near blade

20 m. Crown open, lightly branched. **Bark** smooth but ridged, greyish at base of older trees

Leaves usually downy and coppery when opening; soon glabrous and green, turning gold in autumn

With a natural range extending across the Eurasian landmass, this hardy species grows equally well on exposed high ground or wet lowland where its practice of suckering profusely helps to colonize and consolidate the soil. Aspen's distinctive petiole allows the slightest breeze to reveal its leaf underside.

74

Black poplars

Populus nigra

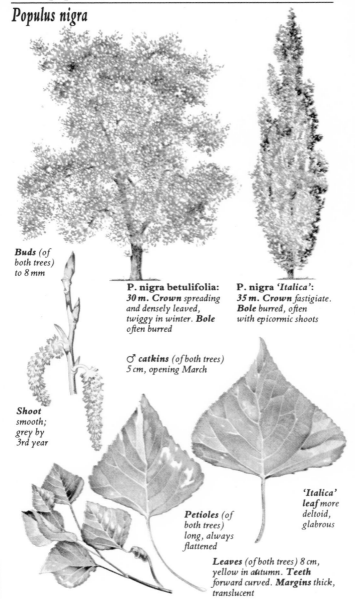

Buds *(of both trees) to 8 mm*

P. nigra betulifolia: *30 m.* **Crown** *spreading and densely leaved, twiggy in winter.* **Bole** *often burred*

P. nigra 'Italica': *35 m.* **Crown** *fastigiate.* **Bole** *burred, often with epicormic shoots*

♂ **catkins** *(of both trees) 5 cm, opening March*

Shoot *smooth; grey by 3rd year*

Petioles *(of both trees) long, always flattened*

'Italica' **leaf** *more deltoid, glabrous*

Leaves *(of both trees) 8 cm, yellow in autumn.* **Teeth** *forward curved.* **Margins** *thick, translucent*

The black poplar normally encountered in Britain is *P. nigra* var. *betulifolia* and differs from its rarer continental type (*P. nigra*) in having birch-like leaves and initially downy twigs and leaf stalks. Its burred bole is diagnostic. The more common Lombardy poplar (*P. n.* 'Italica') may have arisen in central Asia rather than northern Italy as its name implies. The similar 'Plantierensis' clone has a leafier, slightly broader crown and initially pubescent petioles and shoots, nearly glabrous by midsummer. *Pemphigus bursarinus* aphids often attack these poplars and produce distinctively spiralled galls on their leaf stalks.

Populus x *euramericana*

Railway poplar (P. 'Regenerata'): 30 m.
Crown *(left) has bunched foliage.* **Bark** *shallowly fissured.* **Leaf** *(above) 8 cm, opening pale brown.* **Petiole** *5 cm, flattened.* **Catkins** *cottony by July when they fall*

Black Italian poplar (P. 'Serotina'):
40 m. Crown *(right) wide, untidy, asymmetrical.* **Branches** *heavy, curve inwards.* **Bole** *long.* **Bark** *deeply fissured.* **Leaf** *(below) 8 cm, emerges red-brown in May — very late, after catkins.* **Margins** *thickened, translucent.* **Petiole** *6 cm, flattened, sometimes with 1 or 2 glands near blade base*

P. 'Serotina Aurea':
Leaf *golden, turning yellow-green by autumn*

'Robusta': Shoot *downy at first, ribbed.* **Buds** *long, sticky, adpressed.* **Catkins** *numerous in April*

'Robusta': 40 m. Crown *leafier, more regular than 'Serotina'.* **Leaf** *9 cm, opening orange, soon glossy green.* **Petiole** *9 cm, minutely downy.*

Hybrid black poplars have been developed from vegetative cuttings taken from crossings of *Populus nigra* (p75) and the closely related American cottonwood (*P. deltoides*). As clones they are either male or female trees and while technically cultivars of *P.* x *euramericana*, are more usually known by their varietal names. Of the hybrids shown here, 'Regenerata' is the only female, 'Serotina' the most widespread and 'Robusta' the fastest growing. Their hybrid vigour, clean, unburred boles and a resistance to disease make such black poplars important for their timber.

P. trichocarpa • *P. balsamifera* • *P. x candicans*

Western balsam: ♂ **catkin** *(right) long and thick, 8 × 1.5 cm, appearing in April before leaves.* **Buds** *2 cm, adpressed, resinous, slightly pubescent.* **Fruit** *(above) 3-valved, hairy, cottony by May when it is shed*

Western balsam (P. trichocarpa): *35 m.* **Crown** *conic.* **Branches** *whorled, numerous.* **Leaves** *(right) large, 15–30 cm, thick, yellow in autumn, always yellowish-white below.* **Petioles** *3 cm, stout round*

Eastern balsam (P. balsamifera): Shoot *(right) round, not angled.* **Buds** *longer than those of Western balsam, adpressed.* **Leaves** *(below) 12 cm, broader, more obtuse than Western balsam but very variable.* **Blades** *glabrous, slightly downy below, finely serrate.* **Petioles** *7 cm, round*

Balm of Gilead poplar (P. x candicans): Leaves *(above) 15 cm, downy beneath.* **Margins** *ciliate.* **Petioles** *7 cm, downy, roundish.* **Shoot** *hairy initially, angular.* **'Aurora' summer leaves** *(top) develop cream-white and pink marbling*

These trees are recognizable by the balsamiferous odour pervaded by their large, resinous buds and new foliage in early summer. Their leaves are always yellow-white below and have neither flattened leaf stalks nor translucent margins. Western and Eastern balsams are both native to North America and are fast-growing, the latter putting out suckers around its bole. Balm of Gilead poplar produces these so easily and profusely that they soon become a nuisance, and since its trunk is also prone to bacterial canker, its planting is not recommended; the 'Aurora' form, with variegated foliage, is preferable. The Chinese balsam poplar (*P. szechuanica*) is notable for its very large leaves whose undersides are initially downy and purple.

Berlin poplar

Populus x *berolinensis*

Margins translucent. **Teeth** small, rounded

25 m. Crown slender, upswept, densely leaved, producing epicormic shoots.

Bark has pink-brown fissures

Shoot downy initially, with angled tips. **Buds** resinous

Leaves 10 cm, both wedge-shaped and rounded on same shoot, whitish below. **Petiole** 4 cm, round, downy at first, slender

A cross between Lombardy poplar (p75) and Siberian poplar (*P. laurifolia*), from which it derives its rhomboid leaves, this tree is well adapted to severe climatic extremes and is widely planted in continental Europe. Simon poplar (*P. simonsii*), from China, has shorter leaf stalks, obovate leaves and whitish bark.

Necklace poplar

Populus lasiocarpa

♀ **catkin** long, 25 cm, with "beads" of downy fruit

Leaf densely pubescent on underside. **Petiole** 20 cm, round, hairy, stout

Leaves enormous, 35 × 25 cm, with twisted apexes. **Bud** 3 cm, non-sticky. **Shoot** strong, angled, downy

Recognizable at once by the size of its magnificent foliage, this tree is native to moist woodland sites in western China. Its closest relation, *P. wilsoniana*, from the same area, has smaller, sea-green leaves which are not pubescent on their undersides, flattened leaf stalks and buds which are resinous.

Willows *Salix*

Unlike poplars, willows are insect-pollinated, having stiffer, nectar-bearing catkins as well as longer and narrower stipulate leaves, shorter petioles and single-scaled buds. Their shoots lack terminal buds and growth occurs laterally behind the tips.

White willow • Silver willow

Salix alba • *S. alba* 'Sericea'

♂ **catkin** (*of both willows*) *5 cm*

Crown *rounded, densely leaved*

White willow (*above*): **25 m. Branches** *spread.* **Bole** *stout.* **Bark** *cross-ridged, fissured.* **Leaves** (*right*) *8 cm, open light green.* **Blades** *have long, white silky hairs above, densely tomentose on undersides*

Silver willow (*above*): **15 m. Crown** *conic.* **Branches** *ascend.* **Branchlets** *are pendulous.* **Leaves** (*below*) *similar to White willow but slightly wider and more hairy. Shoots and buds are also hairy and appear silvery white*

Teeth *fine.* **Leaf stalk** *short, 5 mm.* **Shoot** *fine, densely haired, not brittle at base.* **Buds** *2 mm, flattened*

Native to most of Europe, this vigorous species is one of the tallest willows and while sometimes confused with Crack willow (p80), can be distinguished by its far less fragile twigs and its less deeply fissured bark. It is often pollarded to produce pliant shoots which are used for basketry. The widely distributed 'Sericea' is readily identified by its colouring and more hairy foliage.

Coral-bark willow

Salix alba 'Chermesina'

Shoots turning orange-red in winter

Buds 2 mm

Shoots very long

Leaves 10 cm, grey-yellowish

Pollarded crown, 10 m, wise narrow conic, 25 m

Habit often more shrubby

Because it is often pruned back heavily to encourage the growth of its long, colourful shoots, this willow seldom reaches its potential height. It is one of several scarlet forms.

Cricket-bat willow

Salix 'Coerulea'

Shoot slender, purplish

Leaves initially hairy

Leaves broader, less hairy than White willow

This vigorous, female tree is probably a hybrid of *S. alba* and *S. fragilis* and its light, resilient wood is ideal for cricket bats.

Crack willow

Salix fragilis

Leaf tip can twist

Petiole 2 cm. **Leaf** to 12 cm (4 times its width), glossy above, glaucous or greyish below; silky at first. **Teeth** far coarser than White willow

♀ **catkin** 10 cm, May

25 m. Crown open. **Bark** deeply fissured

Very similar to *S. alba* and also grown in pollarded form on moist sites, this willow can be distinguished by its larger, more coarsely toothed leaves. Its brittle twigs give the tree its name.

80

Weeping willow

Salix x *chrysocoma*

20 m. Crown broad.
Branches arching.
Shoots very
pendulous, long,
slender, yellow,
becoming brighter in
late winter

Leaves *10 × 1.5 cm, glossy, glaucous below, finely haired on both surfaces, opening in early April*

Catkins *8 cm, often curving up, usually ♂*

Attractive beside water towards which its foliage tends to bend, this is a hybrid of White willow and Chinese weeping willow (*S. babylonica*) which is far less common and has pendulous *brown* shoots and leaves with fewer teeth.

Corkscrew willow

Salix matsudana 'Tortuosa'

Leaves *open in March*

Shoots *"snake" upwards.* **Leaves** *8 cm, crisp, cupped, matt, glaucous below.* **Teeth** *tiny, hooked.* **Margins** *thick*

20 m. Crown open.
Branches curve in "S"
shapes. **Bole** short,
with erect and contorted
stems. **Bark** grey, shiny,
becoming fissured

Useful on dry soils, this willow makes an attractive garden tree. Its leaves are among the first to appear and the last to fall; in winter its distinctively contorted crown, which can only be confused with that of the Corkscrew hazel, is seen to particularly good effect.

81

Salix cinerea • *Salix caprea*

Grey willow leaves 8 cm. **Veins** impressed, hairy below. **Stipules** persist

Grey willow (above): **10 m. Crown** rounded on several stems but variable, can be shrubby

Sallow (right) **10 m. Crown** open. **Bole** often sinuous

Sallow catkins (♂ and ♀) silky in late winter

Sallow leaves to 10 cm, usually obovate but variable, finely pubescent below

Buds 4 mm, red

Petiole dark red

Shoot initially grey with long hairs, but shiny, glabrous, red-brown by winter; unlike Grey willow, not ridged in 2nd year when bark removed

♂ flower (above) 3 cm, opens Mar, before lvs

♀ catkins (right) 5 cm, green when in flower, release fluffy white seeds in May

Grey willow and Sallow belong to a group of intricately related species which are collectively known as Pussy willows. These are most attractive when their catkins begin to expand in late winter and early spring and are the flowering shoots used to decorate churches on Palm Sunday. The willows illustrated here have similar catkins but the shoot of *S. cinerea* remains densely pubescent; its leaves often have rust coloured hairs below, especially in the subspecies *atrocinerea*, which tends to have less downy shoots and is more treelike. All Pussy willows require damp soil for their seeds to germinate.

Osier

Salix viminalis

Catkins 2.5 cm (♂) or 5 cm (mature ♀), set densely on bare twigs, open before leaves

Margins entire, rolled

Shoots long, straight, pliable

Leaf tips twist

Leaves up to 25 cm long, narrow, held at right angles to shoot

Leaf undersides white, intensely downy. **Shoot** initially pubescent

Osier has a wide range both throughout Europe and in Asia as far east as the Himalayas and Siberia. Growing to 10 m as a tree, it is found beside rivers and on other wet sites, where it is grown to produce the flexible wands used in basket-making, the trees being coppiced annually for this. Hoary willow (*S. elaeagnos*) has more slender, feathery leaves up to 15 cm long and curved catkins.

Bay willow

Salix pentandra

Leaves glaucous below. **Teeth** fine, even

Shoot glossy, glabrous. **Buds** 5 mm. **Catkin** 6 cm, erect, appears in May

10 m. Crown low, broad, densely leaved

Leaves 10 cm, glossy with prominent midrib, fragrant when young. **Petiole** 8 mm

Notable for its dark, glossy leaves and the lateness of its flowers which appear in late May, this tree grows throughout Europe and western Asia. Violet willow (*S. daphnoides*) has white lanceolate leaves, male catkins and a purplish bloom on its winter twigs.

Walnut family Juglandaceae

This is a group of large trees with pinnate leaves and male catkins which hang on the tree through winter. The fruit, usually edible, is a drupe or nut and in *Juglans* and *Pterocarya* the pith is chambered.

Walnut

Juglans regia

Leaves 45 cm, pinnate.
Leaflets (5–9) to 18 cm.
Catkins before leaves

Leaf margins entire

Leaflets subsessile, except terminal

Fruit ripe by September, husk withering to expose hardened nut

Fruit 5 cm. **Seed** wrinkled

25 m. Crown wide, rounded. **Branches** low, very sinuous, heavy

Bark in smooth plates between wide fissures. **Bole** upright

Shoot stout. **Pith** chambered. **Buds** 6 mm, aromatic when rubbed

Walnut has become widely naturalized throughout Europe and across Asia and been cultivated since the earliest times, although its exact origin is unknown. Large orchards of it exist in France and California. The fruit is either picked for pickling before the end of July while still fleshy or left until autumn when it has hardened. *J. regia* is the only walnut with entire leaflets.

84

Black walnut

Juglans nigra

Fruit *5 cm, hairy.* **Nut** *thick, corrugated*

Shoot *finely pubescent.* **Buds** *1 cm, ovoid, hairy*

Leaves *50 cm, hairy below.* **Leaflets** *(11–23) 12 cm, serrate, open yellow-green*

This North American tree has a dark, cross-furrowed bark and a crown which can reach 30 m and is narrower than that of Walnut. Its larger leaves usually have more leaflets. Butternut (*J. cinerea*) has larger leaves, to 80 cm, and sticky, hairy fruit.

Wingnut

Pterocarya fraxinifolia

Leaf stalk *smooth*

Buds *2 cm, naked, rufous, hairy, often in pairs*

Leaf *60 cm*

Fruit *in pendulous 45 cm racemes, shiny*

Leaflets *(11–27), sessile*

Rachis *round*

Branches *radiate*

Fruit *2 cm, has 2 long cupped wings*

Bole *often multiple*

30 m. Crown *spreading.* **Bark** *furrowed into ridges*

This vigorous tree from western Asia is usually surrounded by suckers and has twigs with chambered piths. It is easily recognized by its naked buds and hanging seed catkins. Rehder wingnut (*P. x rehderiana*) has flanged leaf stalks.

Bitternut

Carya cordiformis

Leaflets *serrate*

25 m.
Crown *more open in older trees*

Branches *slender.* **Bark** *grey, fissured*

Leaves *25 cm.* **Fruit** *4 cm, encloses 4-ribbed nut*

Shoot *slender with white lenticels.* **Buds** *to 2.5 cm, slender, yellow, pubescent*

A species with a wide natural range throughout the eastern USA, this hickory grows to 20 m and is identifiable by the taste of its seeds and its yellow winter buds. Its leaves have up to 11 leaflets that are paler below and turn yellow in autumn. Pignut (*C. glabra*) has unribbed seeds and leaves with 5 glabrous leaflets.

Shagbark hickory

Carya ovata

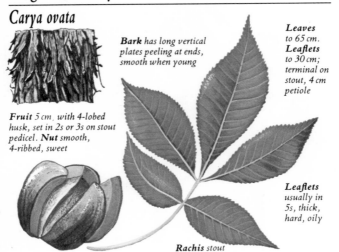

Bark *has long vertical plates peeling at ends, smooth when young*

Leaves *to 65 cm.* **Leaflets** *to 30 cm; terminal on stout, 4 cm petiole*

Fruit *5 cm, with 4-lobed husk, set in 2s or 3s on stout pedicel.* **Nut** *smooth, 4-ribbed, sweet*

Leaflets *usually in 5s, thick, hard, oily*

Rachis *stout*

This species is instantly identifiable by the nature of its bark which begins to flake into long, curling plates when the tree is about 25 years old. Shellbark hickory (*C. laciniosa*) has similar mature bark but its leaves have 7 leaflets with downy undersides.

Birch family Betulaceae

A group of trees and shrubs comprising over 40 species, the members of this family carry male and female catkins on the same tree, the females being small, initially erect when flowering, and held above the males. In *Betula* (pp87–9), *Alnus* (pp90–91) and *Corylus* (p92), the males develop in autumn and are carried over winter, opening to release their pollen before, or when, the leaves appear in spring. Those of *Carpinus* (p93), although pre-formed, are hidden in the winter buds.

Silver birch

Betula pendula

Leaves 7 cm, doubly serrate

Leaves roughish, glabrous below

♂ catkin 3 cm, opens March–April. **♀ catkin** (right) 3 cm, ripens brown

Bole fluted

30 m. Crown narrow. **Branches** ascend when young, later very pendulous. **Bark** smooth, red-brown on young trees

Buds 4 mm. **Shoot** warty

'Dalecarlica': **Leaves** 5 cm. **Margins** deeply dissected. **Petioles** 4 cm, slender

Immature ♂ catkins (above) 2 cm, hang at shoot tip. **Shoot** glabrous, zig-zagged

Seed (above) 2 mm, ripe by Sept, has 2 large wings. **Bract** 7 mm, 3-lobed

'Dalecarlica': Shoots long, very pendulous

With a wide natural distribution throughout most of Europe and Asia Minor, Silver birch is recognizable by its distinctive bark and hairless twigs. It thrives on light, dry and sandy soils, dislikes shade and is plentiful on heaths and moorlands. 'Dalecarlica', from southern Sweden, is one of its graceful cultivars.

Paper birch

Betula papyrifera

Buds 8 mm. **Shoot** warty

Leaves 10 cm but variable, doubly serrate, thick, very matt above. **Petiole** 3 cm, stout, pubescent

20 m. Crown stiff. **Branches** ascend

Leaf underside paler with black glandular dots, hairy on midrib

Catkins with young leaves; ♂ 10 cm when ripe, ♀ erect, smaller

Buds green and brown

Bark exfoliates in paper flakes

Paper birch grows throughout Canada and northern USA; its creamy or pinkish white bark was once used by Indians to cover their canoes. Szechuan birch (*B. platyphylla* var. *szechuanica*) has a chalky white bark and leathery, 12 cm leaves, glaucous below.

Downy birch

Betula pubescens

Leaves 6 cm, coarsely serrate

Buds 6 mm

Leaf undersides paler, hairy on midribs. **Petiole** 6 cm, densely hairy

Fruit 3 cm. **Shoot** hairy, not warty

Young bark typifies that of all young birches

Bark papery, peeling

Downy birch is identifiable by its hairy twigs and is more tolerant of climatic extremes than Silver birch. The 15 cm, doubly serrate leaves of Erman birch (*B. ermanii*), from Japan, are shiny below and have 7–11 pairs of veins.

Himalayan birch

Betula utilis

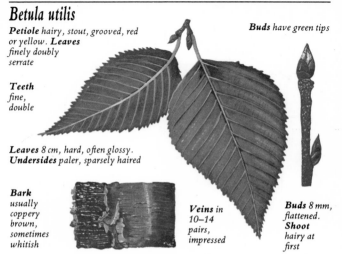

Petiole *hairy, stout, grooved, red or yellow.* **Leaves** *finely doubly serrate*

Teeth *fine, double*

Buds *have green tips*

Leaves *8 cm, hard, often glossy.* **Undersides** *paler, sparsely haired*

Bark *usually coppery brown, sometimes whitish*

Veins *in 10–14 pairs, impressed*

Buds *8 mm, flattened.* **Shoot** *hairy at first*

Recognizable by its shoot, buds and vein count, Himalayan birch has a variably coloured bark which peels away in large sheets. That of Jacquemont birch (*B. jacquemontii*) is bright white while its coarsely serrate leaves have only 7–9 pairs of veins.

Yellow birch

Betula lutea

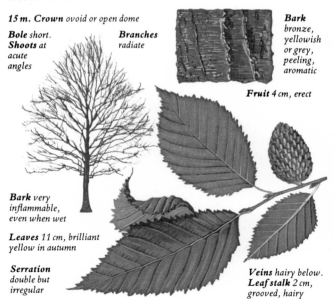

15 m. Crown *ovoid or open dome*

Bole *short.* **Shoots** *at acute angles*

Branches *radiate*

Bark *bronze, yellowish or grey, peeling, aromatic*

Fruit *4 cm, erect*

Bark *very inflammable, even when wet*

Leaves *11 cm, brilliant yellow in autumn*

Serration *double but irregular*

Veins *hairy below.* **Leaf stalk** *2 cm, grooved, hairy*

Native to eastern North America where it can reach 30 m, this birch is notable for its yellow autumn foliage and the long hairs of its leaves and young shoots. Cherry birch (*B. lenta*) has larger, more regularly toothed cordate leaves and thicker, black bark.

Alnus glutinosa

Flowers open on ♂ and ♀ catkins, before leaves, in late March. ♂ **flowers** yellow. ♀ **flowers** 6 mm, erect, red.

♂ catkins 5 cm when fully open

25 m. Crown broad, conic, often on 2 or 3 stems, purplish

Catkins exposed over winter, purple

Bark *fissured, grey, in small plates*

Leaves 10 cm, persist until very end of autumn. **Petiole** 3.5 cm, speckled. **Buds** 7 mm, flat, on 3 mm stalks, narrowed at base, with 2–3 scales

Shoot purple by autumn

Fruit 1.5 cm, ovoid, set in clusters of 1–4

Leaves glabrous, paler below. **Vein axils** tufted

Seed small winged nutlet

Leaf margins slightly waved. **Teeth** irregular, shallow. **Veins** impressed

Fruit woody by time it ripens and releases seeds in October, very persistent as empty "cone"

Alders grow in damp locations and have buoyant seeds that are distributed by water. The deep roots help to conserve river banks and improve the soil with their nitrogen-fixing nodules. The tree survives happily on drier sites but does not regenerate there. 'Laciniata' and 'Imperatis' are forms with deeply lobed leaves.

Grey alder

Alnus incana

Petiole 3 cm

♂ **catkins**
in February

Leaves 10 cm, pointed,
strongly toothed, sometimes
lobulate. **Veins** in
7–12 pairs

♂ **catkins**
10 cm

Leaf underside hairy.
Shoot hairy when young.
Buds 8 mm, stalked

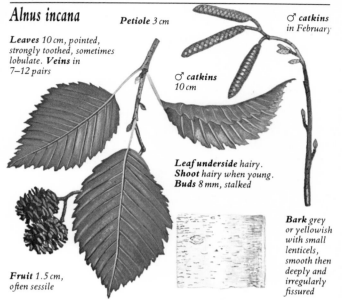

Fruit 1.5 cm,
often sessile

Bark grey
or yellowish
with small
lenticels,
smooth then
deeply and
irregularly
fissured

Grey alder is widely planted on reclaimed sites and can be identified by its pubescent young shoots and the downy undersides of its leaves. Red alder (*A. rubra*) has larger and narrower, distinctly lobed leaves and angled, glabrous shoots.

Italian alder

Alnus cordata

♂ **catkin** 10 cm

Leaf 8 cm, cordate

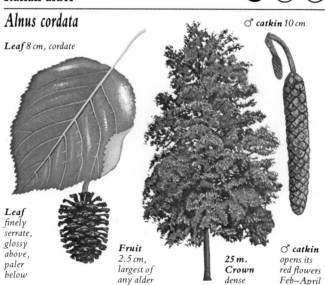

Leaf
finely
serrate,
glossy
above,
paler
below

Fruit
2.5 cm,
largest of
any alder

25 m.
Crown
dense

♂ **catkin**
opens its
red flowers
Feb–April

With a tolerance of urban atmospheres and an ability to grow on drier sites than other alders, this species makes an attractive street tree. It is notable for its almost pear-like leaves with orange axil tufts, sticky twigs and buds and large "cones".

Hazel

Corylus avellana

♂ *catkins* 5 cm, open Feb. ♀ *catkins* 5 mm

Shoot covered in long stiff hairs with swollen tips.
Leaf 10 cm, hairy above and doubly serrate below

Nuts 2 cm,
ripen brown
in clusters
of 1–4

10 m. Crown shrubby

Nuts in papery, toothed bracts

Hazel is a small shrubby tree native to almost all Europe and recognized by its nuts, densely haired twigs and leaves and its plump male catkins. Its female catkins are small and have red styles. 'Contorta', with twisted stems, is a useful ornamental.

Turkish hazel

Corylus colurna

Leaf 15 cm, cordate, glossy

25 m. Crown
regular conic.
Branches very
level, stout,
twisting

Leaf sharply serrate.
Nuts 3 cm, almost covered
by thick, haired husk

Bole stout. **Shoots**
develop corky ridges.
Bark scaly

Turkish hazel is the most tree-like of the genus and its long, deeply lobed bracts (or cupules) almost cover the nuts. Filbert (*C. maxima*), also from the Balkans, has tubular, papery ones almost twice as long as the nuts.

92

Hornbeam

Carpinus betulus

Leaves 12 cm, slightly shiny. **Petiole** 1 cm. **Veins** very impressed, in 15 parallel pairs

Buds 1 cm

Margins finely and doubly serrate. **Leaves** dark green above, yellowish with white tufts below

Fruit 12 cm, in clusters of 8–12 pairs, ripening brown

Buds very adpressed

Seeds 8 mm, exposed at base of bract

Twigs slender, zig-zagged

Catkins overwinter in buds, open with leaves

♀ **catkin** to 3 cm, terminal. ♂ **catkin** to 5 cm, pendent

Bract 3.5 cm, 3-lobed

Catkins expand in March

Bole often fluted. **Bark** grey and silver

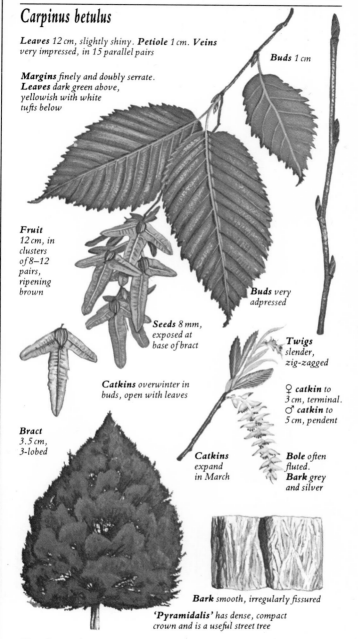

Bark smooth, irregularly fissured

'Pyramidalis' has dense, compact crown and is a useful street tree

Hornbeam is sometimes mistaken for Beech (p94) but closer scrutiny reveals its leaves to be serrate and have parallel and deeply impressed veins. Its smaller buds are set very closely against the shoots; its fruit is very different from that of Beech. Hornbeam is a forest and hedgerow tree that was once rigorously pollarded and coppiced for firewood and highly valued for the hardness and smoothness of its timber.

Beech and oak family Fagaceae

The members of this large, mainly temperate family have simple and alternate leaves and fruit in the form of nuts. These are either fully enclosed by an involucre (or cupule) of fused bracts as in *Fagus*, *Nothofagus* (pp96–7) and *Castanea* (p105), or merely supported by it as in *Quercus* (pp98–104). Male and female flowers are carried in separate catkins on the same tree.

Beech

Fagus sylvatica

Leaves *light green and hairy as emerge, usually dark and shiny, russet in autumn*

Margins *wavy, ciliate at first*

Veins *prominent, in 5–8 pairs*

♂ **catkins** *appear in May as leaves expand, profuse, soon shed*

Nuts *1 cm, shiny, 3-sided, concave*

Shoot *zig-zags, lenticelled.*
Buds *2 cm, spreading.*
Leaves *to 10 cm.*
Petiole *1.5 cm, hairy*

Fruit *2.5 cm, golden green splits in 4 as ripens to brown*

40 m.

Bark *persistently smooth.*
Bole *clean, buttressed.*
Roots *often exposed by erosion*

This majestic tree is instantly recognizable by its smooth bark. Although its natural range includes most of continental Europe and southern Britain, it has been widely planted elsewhere for its timber, and thrives on chalk and limestone. Oriental beech (*F. orientalis*), from the Balkans and Asia Minor, has leafy cupules and broader, larger leaves which have 7–10 pairs of veins.

Some cultivars of Beech

Copper beech ('Purpurea') has strong purple pigments in leaves

Copper beech leaves unfold red or brownish pink but soon become a heavy shade of purple-green

'Purpurea' greener when grown in shade

'Pendula' and **'Dawyck'** both to 30 m tall

Weeping beech ('Pendula') has very pendent shoots on sprawling branches. **Leaves** wide. **Bark** is silver-grey at summit, where it is often exposed

Dawyck beech (*F. sylvatica* 'Dawyck') very fastigiate. **Branches** curving, upswept. Dense Lombardy poplar habit

Petioles 1.5 cm, pubescent

Leaves very deeply cut, hairy below

Leaves to 10 cm

Fern-leaved beech ('Heterophylla') has variable leaves, sometimes willow-like

Beech is noted for the variety of its cultivars. Copper beech, the most common, may have deep purple ('Purpurea') or red leaved clones. Weeping and Dawyck beeches have distinctive habits, 'Heterophylla' remarkable leaves. Others include 'Zlatia', with new foliage golden until July, and 'Rotundifolia' with small, almost round leaves and variegated forms.

95

Southern beeches *Nothofagus*

Nothofagus contains about 40 species, all native to the southern hemisphere and usually differing from true beeches in their smaller fruits with 3 to 7 nutlets, rounder buds, and much smaller, evergreen leaves. Most species are evergreen.

Rauli

Nothofagus procera

Leaves *12 cm, downy on veins below.* **Fruit** *1 cm, "mossy", set singly*

Shoot *warty.* **Buds** *8 mm, conic and adpressed*

Petioles *1 cm*

Fruit *involucre 4-valved releases 1 flat, 2 triangular 7 mm seeds in September*

30 m. Crown *dense*

Branches *stout, ascend steeply, whorled when young.* **Bark** *dull, fissured*

Veins *impressed, in 15–18 pairs*

Margins *slightly waved, very finely toothed*

Leaves *have rounded bases and acute or rounded tips.* **Venation** *very prominent.* **New leaves** *coppery.* **Autumn leaves** *golden red*

Rauli, from the Chilean Andes, is being increasingly planted in the northern hemisphere both for its vigour—on good, well-drained, frost-free sites it can grow 2 m a year—and for the excellent potential of its timber. It can be distinguished from Roblé beech by its stouter shoots, larger and more pointed buds and the more numerous veins of its leaves.

96

Roblé beech

Nothofagus obliqua

Leaves *8 cm, slanted at base, glaucous below*

Margins *are irregularly toothed.* **Veins** *extend to tips of teeth*

Veins *in 7–11 pairs.* **Shoot** *slender*

Petiole *5 mm, red*

Fruit *8 cm, set singly, ribbed, has 3 seeds*

Buds *5 mm, spreading*

30 m. Crown *ovoid, spreading.* **Bark** *fissured*

The Chilean Roblé beech is as vigorous as Rauli but will tolerate drier sites. Antarctic beech (*N. antarctica*) forms a smaller tree, to 15 m, and has crinkled, almost sessile, glossy leaves. These have four pairs of veins which end between two teeth.

Coigue

Nothofagus dombeyi

Buds *1 mm*

25 m. Crown *dense*

Leaves *4 cm, dark, hard, broadest above middle*

Leaves *glossy.* **Undersides** *paler*

Branches *long, splay at summit.* **Bark** *furrowed, scaly.* **Leaf margins** *finely, unevenly serrate*

Coigue is a hardy evergreen from Chile and Argentina. Red beech (*N. fusca*) from New Zealand is also evergreen and has thin, ovate leaves 5 cm long, with coarser, rounded teeth and three or four pairs of veins. They turn red before falling.

Oaks Quercus

This large and important group of noble trees comprises over 400 separate species as well as many hybrids and is found throughout the temperate areas of Europe, Asia and North America. All oaks are noted for their acorns which may ripen over either one or two years and provide the best means of identification. Another is the arrangement of leaves and buds which cluster at the end of shoots and separate *Quercus* from most other genera. Oaks have separate male and female flowers appearing on the same tree; the females are erect but inconspicuous while the males appear in long, pendulous catkins at the same time as the new leaves open. The genus contains both deciduous and evergreen species.

Sessile oak

Quercus petraea

40 m. Crown tall

Branches straight, spreading, radiating. **Bole** long

Buds 6 mm, ovoid, with many finely pubescent scales, set in clusters at shoot tips, open in May. **Shoot** shiny, straighter than that of English oak

Bark thick, vertically fissured

Leaves 12 cm, hard or leathery, widest at middle, very flat, not so prone to caterpillar attack as English oak

Leaf base cuneate, without auricles

Acorns in clusters of 2–6, sessile or on very short peduncles

Petiole to 3 cm

Leaf underside has brownish pubescence on veins

Lobes shallow, in 5–9 pairs

With a long bole that extends well into the crown, this oak can be further distinguished from English oak by its almost stalkless, slightly smaller acorns and the wedge-shaped bases of its leaves. It grows well on light, acidic, stony soil. The similar Downy oak (*Q. pubescens*) has densely hairy leaves and shoots.

English oak
Quercus robur

35 m. Crown *wide*

Foliage *set in bunches*

Branches *large and heavy, very irregular, bear sprouts*

Crown *irregularly domed.* **Bole** *short, very stout.* **Bark** *fissures into tiers of rectangular plates*

Leaves *have auricles at bases.* **Leaf stalk** *1 cm*

Lobes *in 4 or 5 pairs, deeply cut*

Leaves *to 12 cm, widest above middle*

Acorns *2.5 cm, usually in pairs on long, thin peduncle to 10 cm*

Cypress oak *(Q. robur 'Fastigiata') has upswept crown, narrow when young; grows in central Europe*

English oak is very common throughout Europe. It thrives on heavy clay but will do equally well elsewhere including the lighter, stonier soil favoured by *Q. petraea*. Unlike Sessile oak its leaves are glabrous below and have auricles at their bases. Its acorns are carried on long stalks and give the tree its alternative name of Pedunculate oak. Many predators such as the larvae of the Purple hairstreak butterfly (*Quercusia quercus*) attack its young foliage but do no permanent damage since further flushes of growth occur until September.

99

Turkey oak

Quercus cerris

Stipules *long, 2.5 cm, round all buds.* **Shoot** *pubescent*

Bark fissures *shallow; deeper and plating on old trees*

Acorn *large, 2.5 cm, in sessile, "mossy" cup whose 4 mm filaments are parted, pointing upwards on upper half of cup*

Leaves *13 cm, very variable, rough, glossy above, grey, downy below.* **Lobes** *angular, usually in 5–9 pairs*

This hardy native of southern and south-west Europe naturalizes easily and grows vigorously into a mature and massively domed tree which can reach 40 m. It is more upright than *Q. robur* (p99); unlike all other oaks, it has stipules arranged round *all* its buds.

Lucombe oak

Quercus hispanica 'Lucombeana'

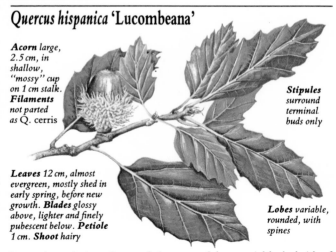

Acorn *large, 2.5 cm, in shallow, "mossy" cup on 1 cm stalk.* **Filaments** *not parted as* Q. cerris

Stipules *surround terminal buds only*

Leaves *12 cm, almost evergreen, mostly shed in early spring, before new growth.* **Blades** *glossy above, lighter and finely pubescent below.* **Petiole** *1 cm.* **Shoot** *hairy*

Lobes *variable, rounded, with spines*

Lucombe oak is a form of the natural but variable hybrid of Turkey oak and Cork oak (p102), inheriting the habit, leaf shape, stipulate buds and acorns of the former species and the bark and semi-evergreen nature of the latter. This tree was first raised by William Lucombe, an Exeter nurseryman, in about 1765.

Algerian oak

Quercus canariensis

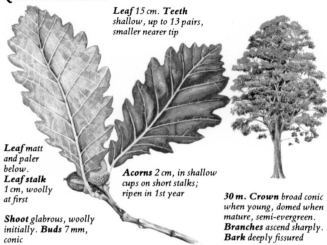

Leaf 15 cm. **Teeth** shallow, up to 13 pairs, smaller nearer tip

Leaf matt and paler below.
Leaf stalk 1 cm, woolly at first

Acorns 2 cm, in shallow cups on short stalks; ripen in 1st year

Shoot glabrous, woolly initially. **Buds** 7 mm, conic

30 m. Crown broad conic when young, domed when mature, semi-evergreen. **Branches** ascend sharply. **Bark** deeply fissured

One of the largest trees to retain a proportion of green leaves throughout the winter, this species is native to north Africa, Spain and Portugal. Caucasian oak (*Q. macranthera*) is similar but its wholly deciduous leaves have more rounded lobes and it carries dark red, shiny buds on pubescent shoots.

Hungarian oak

Quercus frainetto

Buds large, to 1 cm, with many downy scales. **Shoot** downy becoming glabrous; ridged when tree young.

Lobes large, in 7–11 pairs, with lobulate margins. **Sinuses** the most deeply cut of any oak

Leaves large, to 25 cm, with basal auricles. **Blade** sub-glossy above, hairy below. **Petiole** 1 cm, pubescent

30 m. Crown strongly domed. **Branches** radiate. **Bole** stout. **Bark** dark, fissured

Native to south-eastern Europe, this vigorous species is unmistakable in its boldly lobed foliage. Its acorns, similar to those of Algerian oak, ripen in one year. The American White oak (*Q. alba*) also has large, deeply cut leaves but their lobes are more rounded and their petioles up to 2.5 cm long.

101

Cork oak

Quercus suber

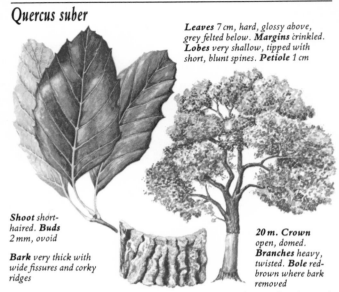

Leaves *7 cm, hard, glossy above, grey felted below.* **Margins** *crinkled.* **Lobes** *very shallow, tipped with short, blunt spines.* **Petiole** *1 cm*

Shoot *short-haired.* **Buds** *2 mm, ovoid*

Bark *very thick with wide fissures and corky ridges*

20 m. Crown *open, domed.* **Branches** *heavy, twisted.* **Bole** *red-brown where bark removed*

The leaves of this Mediterranean tree resemble those of Holm and Turkey oaks (p100). Its useful bark, harvested commercially about every ten years, is similar to that of Lucombe oak (p100) and Chinese cork oak (*Q. variabilis*) whose wholly deciduous leaves have filamented teeth and are silvery-grey below.

Holm oak

Quercus ilex

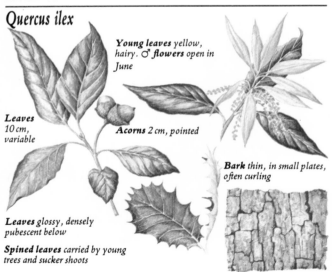

Young leaves *yellow, hairy.* ♂ **flowers** *open in June*

Leaves *10 cm, variable*

Acorns *2 cm, pointed*

Bark *thin, in small plates, often curling*

Leaves *glossy, densely pubescent below*

Spined leaves *carried by young trees and sucker shoots*

A broadly domed species reaching up to 30 m, the sombre Holm oak becomes brighter for a brief period in June when its new, yellowish leaves open. Kermes oak (*Q. coccifera*) is another native of the Mediterranean and hosts the Kermes insect from which scarlet grain dye is prepared. Its leaves are Holly-like.

Red oak

Quercus rubra

Lobes *very variable*

Filaments *3 mm, extend from main veins*

Acorn *2.5 cm, on 1 cm stalk.* **Cup** *shallow*

Bark *smooth, silvery-grey, becoming fissured*

Vein axils *often tufted*

Leaves *to 20 cm, matt both sides.* **Leaf stalk** *2.5 cm.* **Shoot** *ridged*

Glorious in the autumnal hues which give it its name, this sturdy species from the eastern USA typifies a large group of New World oaks which have filamented leaves and smoothish barks. Red oak has heavy branches and grows vigorously to produce a broadly domed crown reaching 35 m.

Scarlet oak

Quercus coccinea

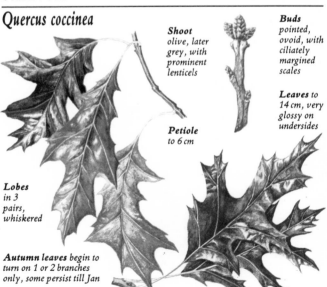

Shoot *olive, later grey, with prominent lenticels*

Buds *pointed, ovoid, with ciliately margined scales*

Leaves *to 14 cm, very glossy on undersides*

Petiole *to 6 cm*

Lobes *in 3 pairs, whiskered*

Autumn leaves *begin to turn on 1 or 2 branches only, some persist till Jan*

A native of eastern North America, Scarlet oak usually has less intense autumnal foliage when grown in Europe, and is less common than Red oak from which it can be distinguished by its smaller, glossy, more deeply lobed leaves and smaller acorns. Its bud scales have pubescent margins and it grows to 25 m.

Pin oak

Quercus palustris

New leaves bright yellow, emerging with flowers in early May. **Buds** 3 mm

♂ **catkins** to 7 cm, appear in early May

25 m. Crown narrow. **Branches** slender, long, pendulous in lower crown

Leaves 15 cm, shiny above, paler below. **Axil tufts** prominent

Acorns 1.5 cm, nearly sessile

Lobes toothed, spined

Sinuses wide. **Buds** glabrous

Small pin-like branches which sometimes grow on its bole help to identify this tree in winter. Its prominent axillary tufts and its shallow acorn cups are also distinctive. Pin oak's narrowly lobed leaves turn red in autumn but not as richly as some of its cousins. Northern pin oak (*Q. ellipsoidalis*) has sessile acorns to 2.5 cm.

Willow oak

Quercus phellos

Leaf 12 cm. **Petiole** 4 mm

Acorn 1 cm, nearly sessile

Leaves entire

From the south-eastern USA. Willow oak has foliage which opens yellow and becomes golden in autumn. Schoch oak (*Q. x schochiana*) is its hybrid with Pin oak and has leaves with one or two lobes. Shingle oak (*Q. imbricaria*) has wider, entire leaves.

Sweet chestnut

Castanea sativa

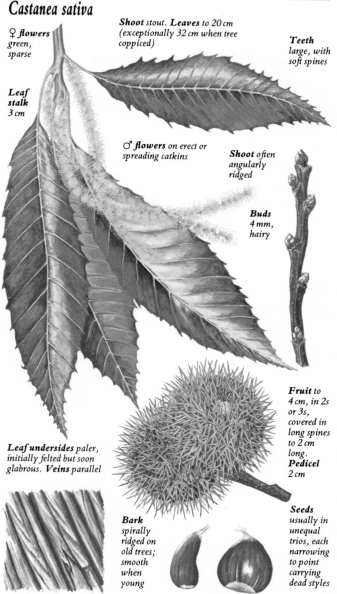

♀ flowers green, sparse

Shoot stout. **Leaves** to 20 cm (exceptionally 32 cm when tree coppiced)

Teeth large, with soft spines

Leaf stalk 3 cm

♂ flowers on erect or spreading catkins

Shoot often angularly ridged

Buds 4 mm, hairy

Fruit to 4 cm, in 2s or 3s, covered in long spines to 2 cm long. **Pedicel** 2 cm

Leaf undersides paler, initially felted but soon glabrous. **Veins** parallel

Bark spirally ridged on old trees; smooth when young

Seeds usually in unequal trios, each narrowing to point carrying dead styles

This Mediterranean tree has a crown which can reach 30 m and a girth that can sometimes exceed 13 m. Exceptional in its vigour, it is often grown for the strong shoots it produces when coppiced. Although closely related to the oaks it differs from them in the female flowers it carries at the base of some male catkins. They open in late June, well after the leaves have appeared. Its buds are not carried in terminal clusters like those of *Quercus*, two members of which, Lebanon oak (*Q. libani*) and Chestnut-leaved oak (*Q. castaneifolia*) have similar leaves to Sweet chestnut.

105

Elm family Ulmaceae

This distinctive group of trees and shrubs is found in both hemispheres and comprises about 15 genera of which *Ulmus* and *Zelkova* are the two most frequently encountered in Europe. The family is characterized by undivided, usually oblique, leaves that are carried alternately and often have rough surfaces and buds with overlapping scales. Its flowers are usually perfect, have many stamens and appear with or before the leaves. Their ovaries have one ovule. Elms have fruit in the form of a broad samara; that of zelkovas is a small nutlet.

Dutch elm disease

This disease has now killed 17 million out of an estimated population of 23 million of what was once England's commonest tree, and sanitation felling, to stop it spreading further, has been abandoned. The English elm has been worst affected; the name of the disease refers neither to the Dutch elm nor to the origin of the fungus, which is probably in eastern Asia, but to the fact that Dutch scientists were the first to research into it.

The aggressive strain of the disease which has caused this damage was imported into Britain in American timber, and lives in the water-conducting vessels in the outer wood of a tree, where it is usually introduced by the elm bark beetles. Their young strip bark patches from young twigs, usually in the upper crown, during their "maturation feeding", and if spores of the fungus are present they will quickly germinate in the wound. Before long the branch will die, and turn brown or autumn gold. The second method of spreading is via the roots, which are often attached to those of nearby elms, and to the suckers they often produce. Even any new suckers which manage to survive into maturity will have no immunity. The beetles will often breed in the inner bark of dead elms, and the illustration on the right shows the galleries produced by the larvae as they eat their way out from the central mother gallery where the eggs were laid.

The notorious Dutch elm disease is a microscopic fungus, *Ceratocystis ulmi*, carried by two elm bark beetles, *Scolytus scolytus* and the smaller species *Scolytus multistriatus* (shown right magnified × 8½).

Replacement of elms

Despite the tragedy, the future for elms is not entirely bleak. Some trees are highly resistant to the disease and by breeding it should be possible to obtain attractive and immune elms. Some of these trees have recently been released, but whether we have the correct answer will not be known for some years. One now being planted is 'Sapporo Autumn Gold', a hybrid of *Ulmus pumila* with *U. japonica*, and others being released include 'Jacan', 'Thomson' and 'Mitsui Centennial'. It is also thought that Asiatic elms such as *U. parvifolia* are immune, and there are plans to import these.

English elm

Ulmus procera

Shoot *slender, zig-zags.* **Buds** *3 mm, slightly hairy*

40 m. Crown *narrow, billowing*

Crown *broadest at top*

Branches *heavy, large, ascending*

Crown *in leaf most dense of all elms.* **Bole** *straight, grows through to top of crown*

Bole *massive, burred.* **Bark** *finely cracked into small plates, dark brown*

Leaves *short-tipped.* **Veins** *in 10–12 pairs*

Shoot *hairy*

Flower *bisexual, opens Feb–March, before leaves*

Leaves *to 10 cm, thick, rounded, obliquely based.* **Petiole** *5 mm, downy*

Shoot *densely hairy*

Teeth *double, sharp*

Leaves *rough above, densely hairy below, remain green until November*

Fruit *1.2 cm.* **Seeds** *not set centrally*

Until recently the most common English tree, this elm was widely planted in the eighteenth century as a hedgerow timber tree. Its origins, however, remain an enigma; it was either a very early introduction or may have arisen as a hybrid. Fertile seeds are rarely set and reproduction is entirely by root suckering. Fluttering elm (*U. laevis*) has very long peduncles.

Wych elm

Ulmus glabra

Leaves *large, 18 cm, variable*

Leaf tips *acuminate*

Shoot *stout, densely haired.* **Buds** *large, 6 mm, hairy*

Seeds *central*

Fruit *1.5 cm*

Bases *oblique.* **Petiole** *5 mm, usually hidden by leaf base*

Fruit *slightly notched, pale green in April when appears before leaves, shed in July when ripe*

40 m. Crown *broad, domed.* **Branches** *arch.* **Bole** *short, stout, heavily buttressed, burred*

Bark *broadly ridged and cracked; silvery-grey, smooth, shiny on young trees.* **Suckers** *rare*

Although sometimes shrubby on exposed sites, Wych elm is renowned for its majestic, spreading crown which is especially attractive in autumn. Its botanical name derives from the smoothness of its *young* bark and not from the leaves, which are very rough above. Most Wych elm seeds are fertile and it very rarely produces suckers. The fruit, appearing well before the foliage, is often produced so abundantly that the tree appears to be fully clothed. It is native to most of Europe and western Asia and the only elm unquestionably indigenous to Britain.

Some cultivars of Wych elm

Camperdown elm *(left and below):* **20 m. Crown** *even*

Camperdown foliage *dense.* **Leaves** *large, 20 cm.* **Branches** *pendent, tortuous*

Camperdown branches *are grafted to Wych elm bole*

'Lutescen' leaves *large, 20 cm*

'Lutescens' leaves *pale in summer*

'Pendula': *12 m, asymmetrical, branches less pendent*

These compact, relatively small forms make ideal garden trees. Camperdown elm is the most common and has a more symmetrical crown than 'Pendula', whose branches form "herringbone" patterns. 'Lutescens' reaches 12 m.

Siberian elm

Ulmus pumila

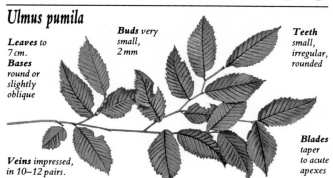

Leaves *to 7 cm.* **Bases** *round or slightly oblique*

Buds *very small, 2 mm*

Teeth *small, irregular, rounded*

Veins *impressed, in 10–12 pairs.* **Petiole** *long, 5 mm*

Blades *taper to acute apexes*

Almost evergreen and apparently very resistant to Dutch elm disease, Siberian elm grows fairly quickly into a small, flat-domed, leafy tree. Chinese elm (*U. parvifolia*) has much smaller, greener leaves, hairy shoots and flowers in September.

109

Ulmus carpinifolia

Seed 1.5 cm, has closed apical notch

Leaves 12 cm, shiny above, glabrous below

30 m. Crown variably domed. *Branches* ascend in arches. *Branchlets* long, pendulous. *Bark* fissured. *Buds* large, 5 mm

Veins have white axil tufts

Leaf base very oblique

Cornish elm: 35 m. Crown vase-shaped. *Branches* form "fan" at apex. *Foliage* dense, carried above branches

Wheatley elm: 35 m. Crown evenly conic. *Branches* set at c. 45°. *Leaves* (above) longer, rounder than Cornish elm

Native to most of Europe, this hedgerow tree was probably introduced to southern Britain as a boundary marker in the first century BC and regional varieties — sometimes classified as species — have developed since then. Those most often seen are Wheatley (or Jersey) elm (*U.c.* var. *sarniensis*), planted in avenues, and Cornish elm (*U.c.* var. *cornubiensis*) which occurs "wild" in south-west England and southern Ireland. Its leaves are cupped and smaller than those of Wheatley elm.

Dutch elm

Ulmus x *hollandica* 'Hollandica'

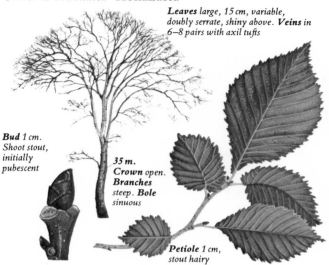

Leaves *large, 15 cm, variable, doubly serrate, shiny above.* **Veins** *in 6–8 pairs with axil tufts*

Bud *1 cm. Shoot stout, initially pubescent*

35 m. Crown *open.* **Branches** *steep.* **Bole** *sinuous*

Petiole *1 cm, stout hairy*

U. x *hollandica* covers all natural hybrids between *U. glabra* (p108) and *U. carpinifolia*. U. x *hollandica* is the species most common in the Low Countries but rare in Britain except as a planted tree; it suckers vigorously and produces epicormic shoots with facility.

Huntingdon elm

Ulmus x *hollandica* 'Vegeta'

35 m. Crown *tall.* **Branches** *straight, often suckering.* **Leaves** *12 cm, smooth.*

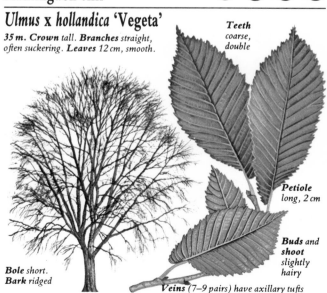

Teeth *coarse, double*

Petiole *long, 2 cm*

Buds *and* **shoot** *slightly hairy*

Bole *short.* **Bark** *ridged*

Veins *(7–9 pairs) have axillary tufts*

First propagated in 1760, this magnificent tree can be identified by the very oblique bases of its large, doubly serrate leaves and the brown axil tufts of their undersides. It is one of the forms more resistant to Dutch elm disease.

Caucasian elm

Zelkova carpinifolia

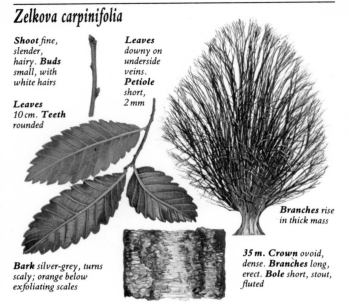

Shoot *fine, slender, hairy.* **Buds** *small, with white hairs*

Leaves *10 cm.* **Teeth** *rounded*

Leaves *downy on underside veins.* **Petiole** *short, 2 mm*

Branches *rise in thick mass*

Bark *silver-grey, turns scaly; orange below exfoliating scales*

35 m. Crown *ovoid, dense.* **Branches** *long, erect.* **Bole** *short, stout, fluted*

Perhaps the most common member of the hardy Zelkova genus, Caucasian elm has smaller leaves with more rounded teeth than Keaki, with which it is sometimes confused, and a distinctive habit. Cretan zelkova (*Z. abelicea*) is a small tree or shrub whose 3 cm leaves are nearly sessile. Its fruit is downy.

Keaki

Zelkova serrata

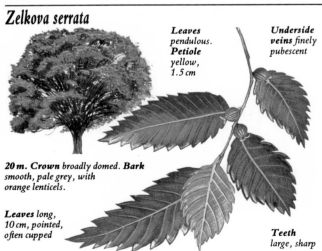

Leaves *pendulous.* **Petiole** *yellow, 1.5 cm*

Underside veins *finely pubescent*

20 m. Crown *broadly domed.* **Bark** *smooth, pale grey, with orange lenticels.*

Leaves *long, 10 cm, pointed, often cupped*

Teeth *large, sharp*

Much prized in its native Japan for the quality of its timber, Keaki shares the steel-grey and orange bark of Caucasian elm but is a less imposing tree. Its larger leaves have pointed teeth and longer petioles and assume autumn shades of yellow, pink and bronze. Its fine zig-zagged shoots carry minute 1 mm buds.

Mulberry family Moraceae

All the members of this family have milky saps but differ in the way their fleshy fruit develops. In *Morus*, this is a cluster of drupes evolving from its flower sepals whereas the flesh of *Broussonetia*'s fruit derives from the stalk of the ovary.

Mulberry

Morus nigra

Buds *6 mm, shiny, red or purplish-brown*

Shoot *stout, hairy, with large lenticels*

10 m. Crown *low, rounded.* **Branches** *twisted.* **Bole** *short, often leans.* **Bark** *stringy, fissured, orange-brown, with many burrs*

Fruit *1.5 cm, ripens from green to red, then finally purplish-black by late August*

Leaves *15 cm, rough, glossy and hairy above, paler, downy below.* **Petiole** *2 cm, stout, hairy*

Leaf *deeply cordate, occasionally 3-lobed*

Leaves *often curled*

Believed to be of Chinese origin, Black mulberry has been cultivated for thousands of years for its sweet but tangy raspberry-like fruit. It has been widely planted in Europe and is usually propagated from cuttings. From Japan and China, Paper mulberry (*Broussonetia papyrifia*) has leaves which resemble those of Mulberry but are densely downy below; its fruit and catkins hang in globular heads. The bark is made into cloth and paper.

White mulberry

Morus alba

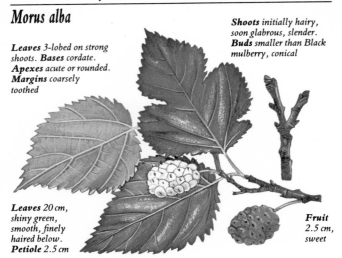

Leaves 3-lobed on strong shoots. **Bases** cordate. **Apexes** acute or rounded. **Margins** coarsely toothed

Shoots initially hairy, soon glabrous, slender. **Buds** smaller than Black mulberry, conical

Leaves 20 cm, shiny green, smooth, finely haired below. **Petiole** 2.5 cm

Fruit 2.5 cm, sweet

White mulberry is a small Chinese tree reaching up to 16 m. It is the preferred food of the silkworm caterpillar for which it is cultivated in southern Europe, China and Japan. The fruit, although sweet, is insipid and not as agreeable as that of Black mulberry. It ripens from green to white, pinkish or violet purple.

Fig

Ficus carica

Leaves 20 cm, usually deeply lobed but occasionally unlobed cordate

Leaves shiny, white hairs on veins below. **Bark** smooth, patterned grey

Fruit 4 cm. **Seeds** enclosed in tasty flesh

Shoot stout, glabrous, ridged. **Bud** conic, acute, laterally squat

Fruit pear-shaped, taking 2 years to ripen from green to purple-black

Fig is a native of southern Europe and forms a spreading tree, to 8 m. It produces fruit developing from a modified shoot tip and fertilization is effected by a small wasp which breeds in the young fruit. In Britain, the wasp does not survive and only the Adriatic form, which needs no fertilizing, produces ripe fruit.

Katsura family Cercidiphyllaceae
Katsura

Cercidiphyllum japonicum

Leaves *8 cm, cordate, glabrous, glaucous.*
Apexes *variable*

Leaf veins
palmate on spur shoots, pinnate on long shoots, in 5s or 7s

Teeth
shallow

Petiole
4 cm, red

Fruit *4 cm sessile pods, ripen brown*

25 m. Crown
columnar.
Stem *often divides.*
Branches
light.
Bark
fissured

Shoot
sub-shiny, glabrous, thickened below buds.
Lenticels
round.
Buds
6 mm

Spur shoots *short, slow-growing*

Katsura, native to central China and Japan, is noted for the brilliance of its autumn colour and for its bright pink young leaves which soon turn fresh green. Its leaves are similar to those of *Cercis* (p145), hence *Cercidiphyllum* (=Cercis leaf), but it is actually in a different family which contains only one other species. This is *C. magnificum* which has larger leaves, two-winged seeds and is found only in Japan.

115

Magnolia family Magnoliaceae

Magnolia

Magnolia x soulangeana

Fruit *comprises spirally set carpels, each splitting to release 1 or 2 seeds*

Leaves *15 cm (larger in some forms), downy below*

10 m. Crown *low*

Leaves *tapered at both base and apex, russet in autumn*

Flowers *to 20 cm.* **Petals** *(6–9) each 10 cm*

Bole *short.* **Bark** *smooth, grey.* **Flowers** *before or with new leaves*

The classic magnolia, first raised in France, is a hybrid of two wild Chinese species, *M. denudata* and *M. lilliflora*. The latter's 'Nigra' cultivar is compact and shrubby and often produces a second crop of its red-purple flowers in late summer.

Campbell magnolia

Magnolia campbellii

Flowers *30 cm, with 12–16 pink or white petals, appear before new reddish leaves*

Shoot *stout*

Leaves *to 20 cm, 11 cm broad*

Buds *4 cm.* **Flower buds** *fat, densely hairy.* **Shoot** *sea green.* **Buds** *conic*

Between February and April, this Himalayan tree carries its magnificent flowers on bare shoots, as do two Chinese cousins, Sprenger magnolia (*M. sprengeri*), with broader leaves, and Sargent magnolia (*M. sargentiana*), with obliquely cuneate ones.

Southern magnolia

Magnolia grandiflora

Fruit *10 cm, on stout 1.5 cm stalk, hairy*

Petiole *2.5 cm, stout, hairy*

Flowers *25 cm, from July to November*

Leaves *20 cm, thick, leathery, shiny, laurel-like, rufously pubescent below*

This small evergreen from the southern USA can be grown in less warm climates but may require the shelter of a wall to survive and flower. The Chinese Delavay magnolia (*M. delavayi*), also evergreen, has larger, very wide, matt, sea-green leaves.

Japanese magnolia

Magnolia kobus

Base branches *regularly clothed in white flowers on older trees; younger trees shy to flower*

Leaves *15 cm.* **Shoot** *shiny, greenish-brown*

Leaves *crinkled, shiny below.* **Veins** *impressed.* **Petiole** *1.5 cm*

15 m. Crown *of young trees broad and conic, becoming domed.* **Branches** *level*

Flowers *12 cm*

Flowers *carried profusely, appear in April, before leaves*

This small species reaches 12 m and has slender, curved leaf buds and grey, downy flower buds. Its shoots are fragrant when crushed. *M. kobus* var. *borealis* is hardier and has pointed leaves. Those of Willow magnolia (*M. salicifolia*), also from Japan, are slender while its crown is an elegant, narrow dome.

Cucumber tree

Magnolia acuminata

Flowers *5 cm.* **Petals** *8 cm, in 2 erect rings of 3, opening dull greenish yellow*

Leaves *to 23 cm, entire, fresh yellow-green above, pale, usually hairy below*

Margins *often wavy*

Leaf margins *entire*

Shoot *stout, glabrous.* **Petiole** *3.5 cm, hairy*

Side buds *smaller*

Bud *to 1.5 cm, downy*

Fruit *8 cm, pink, later bright red, very erect, drops Sept*

From south-western USA and named after the resemblance of its young seed clusters to cucumbers, this stately tree grows to about 25 m. Wilson magnolia (*M. wilsonii*), from China, hardly reaches a third of this and produces hanging, pure white flowers.

Sweet bay

Magnolia virginiana

Fruit *5 cm, comprising 6 mm flattened seeds.* **Leaves** *bluntly tipped with prominent midribs*

Flowers *to 7.5 cm, fragrant, June–Sept on leafy spur shoots*

Leaves *to 15 cm, shiny above*

Petioles *2 cm, slender.* **Shoot** *lenticelled*

Leaf underside *glaucous, pubescent, minutely warty*

Sweet bay is native to the coastal swamps and rivers of south-eastern USA and evergreen in the southern part of this range. In the late seventeenth century it was the first magnolia grown in Europe where its small flowers sometimes persist till December.

Tulip tree

Liriodendron tulipifera

Buds *1 cm, flat, obovoid with 2 purple scales, stalked.* **Shoot** *shiny.* **Leaf scars** *very prominent*

Leaves *15 cm, usually 4-lobed, glabrous, shiny, glaucous below*

Petiole *10 cm, has 2 prominent stipules*

35 m. Crown *dense, becomes broader, more open with age.* **Branches** *regular*

Native to eastern USA, this species has distinctive leaves and produces yellow-green tulip-shaped flowers in June, followed by erect, spindle-shaped fruits. Chinese tulip tree (*L. chinense*) has thinner leaves which are deeply lobed and minutely warted below.

Embrothrium family Protaceae

Chilean firebush

Embrothrium coccineum

Flowers *5 cm, tubular, comprising 4 linear segments curving back to reveal long anthers.* **Racemes** *10 cm*

Fruit *to 5 cm, woody, on long, red peduncle*

Leaves *15 cm, entire, leathery, glossy above, glaucous green below, shape variable*

15 m. Crown *slender, often on several boles.* **Bark** *smooth*

Chilean firebush is native to Chile and Argentina but grows in Europe as far north as Britain. It is a flamboyant sight in early summer when its newly-opened flowers contrast with the dark, glossy foliage; though vigorous, it is short-lived.

Witch-hazel family Hamamelidaceae

Sweet gum

Liquidambar styraciflua

30 m. Crown broad dome, ovoid-conic when young, turns orange, red or purple in autumn

Leaves 5-rarely 7-lobed, 15 cm, glabrous except axillary tufts

Buds 5 mm, shiny

Bark grey or brown, fissured in squares, furrowed when old. **Leaf margins** with incurved teeth

Shoot woolly at first, round with corky wings

Sweet gum is native to the eastern USA and as far south as Guatemala. The three species in this genus have globose flowers and spiny pendulous fruits, like Plane. Leaves are similar to Maple (pp 154–61) but alternate.

Persian ironwood

Parrotia persica

Flowers before leaves

Shoot green-brown, has short stiff hairs, star-shaped

Leaves with 6–9 pairs impressed veins, brown hairs below

Buds downy, brown or black-purple

Flowers only stamens coloured

Bark similar to that of London plane, peels to expose brown or yellow

Leaf margins waved, glossy

Bark smooth, pink-brown or grey-green, exfoliating in large flakes

Persian ironwood, native to the lush forests around the Caspian sea, can grow to 15 m, but is usually a sprawling shrubby tree. It is attractive in autumn when it assumes gold and crimson tints, and is distinguishable by its unusual bark.

Rose family Rosaceae

The rose family is a large assemblage of trees, shrubs and herbs, with alternate leaves. The family is characterized by the flowers, which have the sepals, petals and stamens attached to the receptacle margin. The ovary may have one or several carpels, and may be either superior, above the petals and stamens, or inferior, below them. Four subfamilies are distinguished by fruit.

Two subfamilies, centred on *Rosa*, the Rose, and *Spirea*, contain only shrubs. *Prunoideae* is defined by having a fruit which is a drupe, a fleshy outer covering around a single bony seed. *Prunus* is the only tree genus, divided into sections based on the flower arrangements.

The subfamily *Pomoidae* has a fruit which is a pome, which has 2–5 carpels containing the seeds within a fleshy covering, and includes many tree genera.

Snowy mespil

Amelanchier lamarckii

Flowers *massed, star-like, with 5 pure white obovate petals, 2 cm, in conical upright racemes*

8 m. Crown *low rounded dome, often on several stems, red in autumn*

Leaves *7 cm, elliptic to oblong-obovate, margins finely toothed, dull green, rounded or cuneate at base, new leaves copper*

Fruit *6 mm, ripens from green to red to purple*

Snowy mespil is a small tree or shrub, now naturalized on sandy heaths in Europe, native to eastern North America. The sweet black fruits are edible when they ripen in July. Amelanchier is a genus of small trees from North America and Asia.

121

Hawthorn

Crataegus monogyna

Leaves *10 cm, deeply lobed, with few teeth.* **Thorns** *to 2.5 cm*

Veins *pinnate.* **Flowers** *in corymbs of up to 16, appear with leaves in May*

15 m. Crown *dense.* **Bole** *short, fluted*

Shoot *purplish, stout.* **Buds** *2 mm, glabrous, set in pairs at bases of spines*

Fruit *1 cm, 1-seeded, has persistent calyx, profusely set, ripening September*

Hawthorn's common names, "May" and "Quickthorn", derive from its flowering season and the speed with which it can form hedges. It has pink-flower cultivars such as 'Pendula Rosea'. Midland hawthorn (*C. oxyacantha*) is less spiny and has shallowly-lobed leaves, two-seeded haws and veins all pointing forward.

Cockspur thorn

Crataegus crus-galli

Leaves *8 cm*

Fruit *1.5 cm, 2-seeded, sometimes persists in winter*

Leaves *serrate, glabrous.* **Shoots and spines** *purple-brown.* **Spines** *to 8 cm*

Native to eastern USA, Cockspur thorn forms a low, rounded tree to 7 m and assumes rich orange tints in autumn. Broadleafed cockspur (*C.* x *prunifolia*) differs in its wider leaves, dark purple-brown shoots and haws that fall in autumn. Lavalle thorn (*C.* x *lavallei*) has shiny, blackish-green leaves that are downy below, pubescent shoots with few thorns and 1.5 cm, orange haws.

Medlar

Mespilus germanica

Flowers *5 cm, sessile, appear with leaves*

Fruit *6 cm, globose with sunken apex.* **Buds** *8 mm, pubescent*

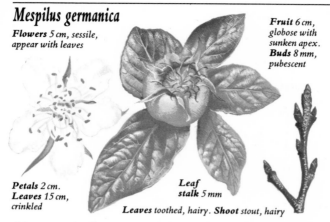

Petals *2 cm.* **Leaves** *15 cm, crinkled*

Leaf stalk *5 mm*

Leaves *toothed, hairy.* **Shoot** *stout, hairy*

A low tree closely related to the hawthorns, Medlar is a native of south–eastern Europe but widely cultivated for its large fruit which has persistent calyxes and becomes palatable after it has been bletted or over-ripened. Its single flowers are sessile.

Tree cotoneaster

Cotoneaster frigidus

15 m. Crown *wide, rounded, sometimes on several stems, often leaning.* **Branches** *arch, then level*

Bark *scaly.* **Fruit** *a pome with 2 nutlets, ripening September, persistent.* **Leaves** *13 cm, soft, entire, semi-evergreen; some forms more crinkled*

Flowers *set in dense 6 cm heads, open June*

Leaves *initially white and hairy on undersides*

Fruit *5 mm*

Recognizable by its pale bark and its short, often leaning, bole, this Himalayan tree is the tallest of the cotoneasters and reaches 17 m. It usually retains some of its leaves throughout winter. Waterer cotoneaster (*C.* x *watereri*) has narrower, glossy leaves with impressed veins. Some forms may have pale yellow fruit.

Rowans and whitebeams *Sorbus*

This genus produces large corymbs of flowers developing into red, white, pink or russet heads of berries. While the leaves of rowans are pinnate, those of whitebeams are simple and entire; some hybrid taxa such as *S.* x *thuringiaca* (p 129) have both types.

Rowan

Sorbus aucuparia

Flowers 1 cm, strongly scented, open in May in flat 15 cm corymbs. **Pedicels** densely hairy

Leaves 20 cm, pinnate. **Leaflets** (11–19), serrate with rounded bases. **Rachis** round

Shoot initially hairy, dull grey-purple

Bark shiny, smooth

Buds 1.7 cm, ovoid, purple with dense grey hairs

15 m. Crown ovoid or columnar conic, irregular. **Branches** ascend or arch

Berries 8 mm

Fruit ripens scarlet very abruptly in August

'Beissneri' leaflets deeply serrate, yellowish-green

'Asplenifolia' leaflets deeply cut by serrate teeth, lobulate at base

'Beissneri' bark orange or pinkish brown when wet, dull grey when dry

Usually a small tree with a fastigiate habit and a dislike of shady sites, Rowan is native throughout Europe and in western Asia and North Africa either in the open or light woodland. Its other name, "Mountain Ash", refers to the apparent similarity of its foliage to that of Ash (p 182) and its ability to grow at up to 2,000 m above sea level. It is often used as a street tree, especially clones such as 'Asplenifolia', 'Beissneri' and 'Xanthocarpa'.

Chinese scarlet rowan

Sorbus 'Embley'

Leaves scarlet, later purple-red in autumn

Shoot glabrous, brown. **Buds** 1.5 cm, pointed, adpressed, shiny, deep red

Fruit 8 mm, orange-red.
Pedicels glabrous, lenticulate.
Crown ovoid, wider with age

Leaf 17 cm, with 11–17 6 cm leaflets
Leaflets doubly serrate, with oblique bases

15 m. Bark silvery-grey, smooth

Of obscure origin, probably Chinese, this rowan is often planted as a street tree under the name *S. discolor* which is a much rarer tree with white fruit. Sargent rowan (*S. sargentiana*), also from China, has 35 cm leaves with impressed veins and stout shoots.

Vilmorin rowan

Sorbus vilmorinii

Petiole scarlet at base

Leaves 12 cm, with 19–33 leaflets. **Rachis** winged. **Fruit** globose, ripens dark maroon then fades through pink to flushed white

Shoot slender, soon glabrous, grey-brown or maroon

Leaves glaucous below

Fruit 1 cm

Fruit hangs in lax corymbs

Buds adpressed, hairy between scales, dark brown

Leaflets 2 cm, with round tips and entire bases

Vilmorin rowan is a small tree growing to about 8 m, recognizable by its fern-like foliage and unusual fading fruit. It is a native of western China, as is *Sorbus* 'Joseph Rock', which grows to 10 m, has amber fruits and purple or crimson autumn tints, and slightly longer leaves although with fewer leaflets.

Hupeh rowan

Sorbus hupehensis

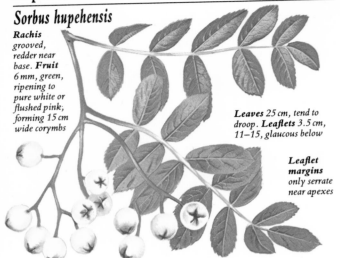

Rachis grooved, redder near base. **Fruit** 6 mm, green, ripening to pure white or flushed pink; forming 15 cm wide corymbs

Leaves 25 cm, tend to droop. **Leaflets** 3.5 cm, 11–15, glaucous below

Leaflet margins only serrate near apexes

A small species of rather gaunt habit, this Chinese tree is noted for its white berries which are often held over winter. Kashmir rowan (*S. cashmiriana*) has ones twice as large and is further identified by pink flowers and leaflets that are entirely serrate.

Service tree

Sorbus domestica

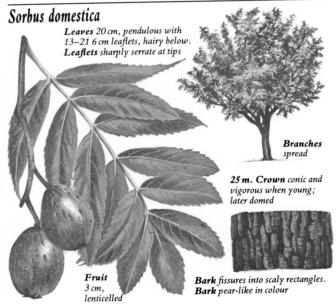

Leaves 20 cm, pendulous with 13–21 6 cm leaflets, hairy below. **Leaflets** sharply serrate at tips

Branches spread

25 m. Crown conic and vigorous when young; later domed

Fruit 3 cm, lenticelled

Bark fissures into scaly rectangles. **Bark** pear-like in colour

This Mediterranean species, the largest member of *Sorbus*, reaches 20 m and is sometimes confused with Rowan (p124). Its apple- or pear-shaped fruit (which is sometimes used for cider-making) is much larger. Larger flowers, resinous buds, a more spreading habit and shredding bark are also keys to identification.

Whitebeam

Sorbus aria

Leaves 8–15 cm.
Petioles 2 cm

20 m. Crown dense. **Branches** upswept. **Leaf undersides** very downy, when turned in wind make tree attractive

Flowers 1.5 cm, in dense 8 cm corymbs in May. **Leaf margins** serrate or lobulate

Bark smooth but fissured

Buds 2 cm, conic, tipped with white hairs. **New leaves** so downy when open (right) that appear almost white. **Shoot** 3 mm thick

Fruit 1.5 cm

S. aria is native to most European chalk and limestone areas and likes open sites, often on woodland fringes. The whiteness of its emerging leaves and the persistent pubescence of their undersides give the species its name. Two forms are widely planted: 'Lutescens' which has very silvery new leaves and 'Decaisneana' with narrow leaves that are 15 cm long.

Himalayan whitebeam

Sorbus cuspidata

'Mitchellii' (below) has very broad leaves

Leaves huge, to 22 × 18 cm

Leaves finely and doubly serrate

Fruit 2 cm, globose or pear-shaped, brown when fully ripe, lenticelled

Leaves tomentose below, shiny above

A vigorous, adaptable species with a broad, erect crown reaching 20 m, this whitebeam is noted for its large leaves that remain silvery below, even when their uppersides have turned russet in autumn. 'Mitchellii' is a cultivar with very broad leaves.

Wild service tree

Sorbus torminalis

Fruit 1 cm, brown with rusty lenticels, ovoid or sub-globose, slightly angled

Shoot shiny, soon glabrous, purplish or olive-brown. **Leaves** 10 cm, shiny, glabrous, finely and doubly serrate, russet in autumn. **Petiole** to 5 cm

Fruit hangs in lax, 12 cm corymbs

Leaf lobes in 3–5 triangular pairs, smaller towards leaf tip. **Venation** pinnate

Fruit leathery

Bark smooth at first, later fissured into scaly plates

This tree is native to most of Europe but in Britain is mainly restricted to southern clay sites. It usually remains small but occasionally attains 20 m. Its leaves are unique in the *Sorbus* genus and resemble those of some maples.

Service tree of Fontainebleau

Sorbus latifolia

Shoot initially woolly, soon shiny, smooth, brown. **Buds** 5 mm, globular, glabrous, olive-brown. **Petiole** 3.5 cm

Leaves large, to 20 × 12 cm

Flowers in broad 10 cm corymbs, open in May. **Pedicels** woolly. **Leaves** glossy above, grey felted below, lobed or coarsely doubly serrate

Fruit 1.3 cm, ellipsoid or globose, yellow or orange-brown, with lenticels

This tree, a hybrid of Wild service tree and Whitebeam, is one of a number of "microspecies" which are apomytic, i.e. their seed is produced without cross-fertilization. Amongst the group are *S. bristolensis*, from the Avon Gorge, Bristol, with narrower, cuneate leaves, and *S. anglica*, with shallowly lobed leaves.

Swedish whitebeam

Sorbus intermedia

Bark *grey or purplish-grey, smooth, fissured*

Buds *greenish or red-brown, hairy, 8 mm.*
Leaves *12 cm, greyish, white woolly below, darker above*

Fruit *1.5 cm, ovoid, glossy green turning to bright scarlet, in bunches of 20*

Leaves *elliptic, rounded, toothed lobes, cut ⅓ or less to midrib*

Native to the Baltic countries, Swedish whitebeam is derived from Rowan and Whitebeam. Arran whitebeam (*S. arranensis*) is only native to two glens on the Scottish island of Arran, and has more deeply lobed leaves. Both are good street trees.

Finnish service tree

Sorbus x thuringiaca 'Fastigiata'

Shoot *grey or purplish, soon glabrous.*
Buds *8 mm, dark red-brown, ovoid or conical, few scales.*
Petiole *red*

Leaves *11 cm, oblong-obovate, usually with 1–2 (rarely as many as 4) free leaflets, grey woolly below, base cuneate*

Lobes *decrease in size towards tip*

15 m. Crown *ovoid, with dense mass of ascending branches.* **Bark** *smooth dull grey, later becoming shallowly cracked*

Leaflets *serrate towards tips*

S. thuringiaca is a cross between Rowan and Whitebeam which accounts for its partly pinnate leaf. The fruit is scarlet, as in Whitebeam, and carried in lax bunches. It is nearly always encountered as the clone 'Fastigiata' which is a useful street tree. It was first recorded in Thuringia, Germany.

Crab apple

Malus sylvestris

Buds *5 mm, grey-haired*

Flowers *2.5 cm wide*

Shoot *sometimes thorny*

Leaves *6 cm*

Leaf stalk *4 cm*

Leaves *paler green below*

Fruit *2.5 cm, globose, yellow-green, ripening to reddish flush*

A native of Britain, western Europe and western Asia, Crab apple has white flowers, faintly flushed pink, and yields a fruit which, while hard and sour, makes excellent jelly. Crab apple is a parent of Orchard apple (*M. domestica*) which has much pinker flowers and sweeter, softer and larger fruit.

Siberian crab

Malus baccata

15 m. Crown *domed.* **Branches** *arch*

Leaves *to 7 cm, narrow, sharply serrate*

Fruit *1 cm, green, ripening to clear red.* **Pedicels** *up to 6 cm, very slender*

Flowers *to 4 cm wide, ivory white with spaced narrow petals*

Petiole *5 cm*

A tree with a wide natural distribution from Siberia through northern China to the Himalayas, this has fruit which persists through winter when the pointed buds also assist identification. Its *mandshurica* variety has broader leaves with hairy petioles.

130

Purple crab

Malus x purpurea

Flowers *4 cm wide, open in early May in 6s and 7s.*
Petals *obovate, darker in bud*

Fruit *small, 2 cm*

The 8 cm leaves of this tree unfold purplish red in May but soon become green and glossier above with their main veins purplish below. The form is sparsely branched and reaches 6 m; its cultivars are bigger and more vigorous and include 'Aldenhamensis', 'Eleyi', 'Lemoinei' and 'Profusion'.

Japanese crab

Malus floribunda

Teeth *coarse*

10 m. Crown *dense.* **Leaves** *to 8 cm, paler and pubescent below, sometimes lobed on vigorous shoots*

Flowers *4 cm, red in bud, fading to pink, then whitish, in umbels of 4–7*

Fruit *2 cm, ripens yellow or red*

Flowers *open in May*

Shoot *hairy, becoming almost glabrous*

Japanese crab is most attractive when displaying both its red buds and its pink and white flowers. Chinese crab (*M. spectabilis*) has broader, glossy leaves and large, pink, semi-double flowers. Neither species has apples with indented bases.

Hupeh crab

Malus hupehensis

Leaves to 10 cm, paler below. **Veins** impressed

Petiole 5 cm

Flowers 4 cm, white with pink flush, in umbels of 3–7

Fruit 1 cm. **Calyx** falls before fruit matures

Bark very fissured

Hupeh crab has shiny, slightly downy, purple shoots and thorny spur shoots. The leaves can be made into a "red tea". It is very attractive in flower and vigorous, growing to 15 m. Sikkim crab (*M. sikkimensis*) has thornier spur shoots and woolly leaves.

Chonosuki crab

Malus tchonoskii

Leaves to 12 cm, opening silvery grey, tomentose

Branches long, very upright

Crown diamond-shaped

Buds rounded

Shoot has white wool, partly lost by autumn

Fruit 2 cm, yellow-green with purple flush

A native of Japan, this makes a good street tree because of its vigorous growth and upright habit. It has brilliant autumn colours. Yunnan crab (*M. yunnamensis*) has yellow-green leaves and 1–2 cm yellow or bright red fruit, speckled white.

Wild pear

Pyrus communis

Petiole *2–5 cm, slender*

Teeth *very fine*

Flowers *4 cm in corymbs 5–8 cm wide, appearing April, before leaves have fully emerged*

Fruit *4 cm, can be globose, has persistent calyx.* **Leaves** *8 cm, variable, glossy, paler below*

Wild pear is native to most of western Europe but most trees encountered have probably hybridized with selected orchard forms. The crown is narrowly conic at first, becoming tall and domed. 'Beech Hill' is spire-like. Chinese pear (*P. calleryana*) has leathery leaves which are hairy on their midrib below.

Willow-leafed pear

Pyrus salicifolia

Leaves *9 × 2 cm, entire, downy at first but soon glossy above*

Flowers *2 cm, opening April, in dense corymbs*

Petiole *1.5 cm, slender*

8 m. Crown *domed.* **Branches** *slender, pendulous*

Fruit *2–3 cm, lenticelled*

A native of the Caucasus, this is usually seen as the 'Pendula' clone, which as a young tree has a distinctly weeping habit. Snow pear (*P. nivalis*), from southern Europe, has broader, less glossy leaves and rounded fruit. It reaches 20 m.

Cherries and Plums *Prunus*

The trees in this genus, which also includes Blackthorn, Peach, Apricot and Almond, have fleshy single-seeded fruit which develops from a single ovary. Most species have up to four glands at the junction of their petioles and leaf bases; those without have shoots which are partially green for two or more years.

Wild cherry

Prunus avium

30 m. Crown *open, conic when young*

Branches *whorled.* **Bole** *straight.* **Bark** *smooth with horizontal lenticels, fissures with age.* **Leaves** *ovate or oblong-ovate*

Fruit *1 cm, ripens July.* **Petiole** *4 cm, grooved, yellow below, with glands at leaf base*

Flowers *to 3.5 cm wide, in umbels of 2–5 on 3–5 cm pedicels, appear with or before leaves in April.* **Shoot** *shiny, purple-brown above, grey-brown on underside*

'Plena' flowers *open May*

'Plena' flowers *double, globose, with 30–40 petals*

Leaves *12 cm.* **Underside veins hairy**

Wild cherry, also called Gean or Mazard, is native to Europe and western Asia and is striking in flower, when its leaves are bronze, and also in autumn when they turn yellow and red. It is cultivated in areas too cold for apples and is the predominant parent of most domestic fruiting cherries. 'Plena' does not set fruit but its larger flowers persist for up to three weeks. Sour cherry (*P. cerasus*) has a shrubbier, suckering habit, glabrous leaves and tart fruit.

Sargent cherry

Prunus sargentii

**10 m.
Branches**
*radiate from
2 m bole.*
Bark
*purplish-
brown*

Flowers
*4 cm, in
sessile
umbels
of 4–6*

Fruit
*1 cm,
ripens
green to
red, then
black by
June.*
Leaves
*15 cm,
unfold
reddish*

Flowers
appear April

Notable for the brilliant reds and scarlets of its early autumn foliage, Sargent cherry is a large tree that reaches 25 m when growing wild in the mountains of Japan. In cultivation, it is usually grafted to a rootstock of Wild cherry and is much smaller.

Autumn cherry

Prunus subhirtella 'Autumnalis'

Leaves *6 cm.*
Veins *hairy
below.* **Leaf
stalk** *1 cm,
dark red, hairy*

**10 m.
Crown** *open*

Shoot
*very
hairy*

Flowers
*2 cm,
in
umbels
of 2–5*

Buds
3 mm

Branches
*densely twigged
when older*

This tree has the invaluable asset of flowering intermittently in winter and its semi-double flowers are carried from October to early spring. It is a cultivar of the Japanese Rosebud cherry which is far less common and only carries flowers in April.

135

Japanese cherries

Individually identifiable by their various flowers and habits, Japanese cherries comprise about forty small trees which have usually been grafted to a Wild cherry rootstock. Of mixed parentage, they are usually discussed as non-specific cultivars of *Prunus* rather than classified as varieties of *Prunus serrulata*, the species from which most have probably been developed. Collectively, they are sometimes referred to as the "Sato Zakura" (domestic cherries).

'Amanogawa'

Flowers 5 cm wide in umbels of 3–6

Flowers semi-double

Petals 6 mm

Flowers densely clustered, open in May with bronze-green leaves

8 m. Crown tightly fastigiate, splaying with age, usually after 6 m. Shoot stout, glabrous. Buds large, 9 mm

'Kanzan'

13 m. Crown usually an "inverted cone" (left). Branches spaced, cross and ascend at 45°, then spread with age (below)

Flowers 5.5 cm wide, in umbels of 3–7. Pedicels 3 cm. Petals 20–30, open in April with bronze new leaves

'Shimidsu'

3 m. Crown low, spreads

Branches often pendent

Flowers 6 cm, pink in bud. Peduncle 6 cm

All Sato Zakura have large leaves up to 20 cm long which turn gold or pink in autumn and shoots as shown. The 'Amanogawa' habit instantly identifies it, as do the ascending and crossing branches of the very common 'Kanzan'; no other cherry is so sprawling in old age. The flowers of 'Shimidsu' are notable for their long penduncles.

'Shirofugen'

Flowers 5 cm, in umbels of 2–4

Petals 20–30

6 m.
Branches arch

'Shirotae'

Flowers 2 cm,
semi-double

9 m. Branches flat, then droop

Flowers droop

'Tai-Haku'

Leaves 20 cm, open golden coppery
12 m

Flowers
6 cm, largest
in genus, in 3s or 4s on 3 cm stalk

Flowers
hang outwards

'Ukon'

Branches sparse, may arch on old trees

Umbels of
2–5 on stout stalk

Leaves open
bronze, soon
green

Flowers 5 cm

'Shirofugen', like 'Shimidsu', flowers very late, in mid-May, but has a vigorous, spreading habit, slightly larger leaves and flowers opening with a pink tinge. The semi-double flowers of 'Shirotae' open a month earlier. 'Ukon' is one of several Japanese cherries with yellow or greenish flowers. 'Tai-Haku' has the largest flowers of any *Prunus* species and is probably closest to the Wild cherry ancestor of the Sato Zakura.

137

Japanese cherries

'Pandora'

Flowers in 3s or 4s on very short stalks

8 m. Flowers 3 cm, single, open early April. **Leaves** open bronze

Habit upright. **Crown** vase-shaped

Bark richly lenti-celled

Fuji cherry

10 m. Crown dense

Flowers 2 cm, single, sessile, 2–4 on 2.5 cm peduncle, appear before leaves

Calyx red

Hillieri 'Spire'

Flowers in mid-April with new reddish leaves

8 m. Crown dense and fastigiate

Flowers 3 cm, single, in umbels of 1–3

'Umineko'

Flowers open April, with fresh green leaves

Stamens golden. **Calyx** purple

10 m. Crown very erect, dense. **Leaves** 9 cm, sharply serrate

Flowers 3–4 cm, single

All these cherries have petals set singly and produce small black fruit. Fuji cherry (*P. incisa*) was crossed with Sargent cherry (p135) to give *P.* x *hillieri*, whose 'Spire' clone is an ideal street tree, and with Oshima cherry (*P. speciosa*) to produce *P.* 'Umineko'. 'Pandora' is another non-specific *Prunus* cultivar (see p136).

Tibetan cherry

Prunus serrula

Flowers 2 cm, in umbels of 2–4, on 4 cm stalks, appear in May. Leaves 12 cm, finely toothed

Bark glossy, with long bands of lenticels on vigorous trees, flaky

Fruit 5 mm, on 4 cm pedicels. Leaves hairy below. Petiole 1 cm

Primarily planted for the magnificence of its bark, Tibetan cherry is also noted for its finely serrate willow-like leaves. These are unique among true cherries. *P.* x *schmittii* has a similar but less spectacular bark, an upright habit and pink flowers.

Yoshino cherry

Prunus x yedoensis

Leaves to 15 cm, finely pubescent below. Shoot slender, hairy

Flowers 3.5 cm, set densely in umbels of 5–6, appear well before leaves, deep pink in bud, soon fade whitish

Fruit 1 cm, on pubescent pedicel, bitter

15 m. Crown low, very spreading. Branches arch, pendulous at tips. Bark grey, darker on large trees

Flowers appear early April, almond-scented

Yoshino is unknown in the wild but is believed to be a hybrid of Rosebud cherry (p135) and Oshima cherry (*P. speciosa*). It is unusual among Japanese flowering cherries in having densely pubescent leaves, flower stalks and shoots. Its fruit is black.

139

Bird cherry

Prunus padus

Flowers *1–1.5 cm, on crowded, irregular 15 cm racemes, open in late May, very fragrant*

Fruit *globular*

Petiole *2 cm, stout, grooved*

Flower racemes *glabrous, semi-erect or drooping, leaves set at base*

Leaf veins *impressed*

Leaves *grey-green below, with axil tufts.* **Teeth** *fine*

Fruit *8 mm, green, ripens red to black, bitter*

Leaves *to 12 cm, stout and leathery, dull*

Bird cherry has a wide distribution from Britain across northern Eurasia to Japan, and is easily recognized when in flower by its semi-erect racemes. Its smooth, dark, bitter-smelling bark was once used to prepare medicinal infusions. This tree has glabrous shoots and pointed and conic 5 mm buds.

Black cherry

Prunus serotina

Margins *wavy*

25 m. Crown *irregularly domed on a few stems.* **Branches** *arch.* **Bark** *aromatic*

Leaves *have 2 glands at base.* **Main vein** *below has basal half with dense white hairs*

Leaves *13 cm, shiny, stout and leathery, dark green above, paler below.* **Buds** *3 mm, adpressed*

Black cherry, one of the largest trees in the genus, grows wild in eastern North America. Its fruit carries persistent calyxes, and its flowers are larger and grow in more erect racemes than those of Bird cherry. Its serrate, glossy leaves and its smaller buds also distinguish it. Its leaves are held late and fall yellow.

Cherry laurel

Prunus laurocerasus

Flowers *in short racemes, appear January, open April.*
Fruit *2 cm, ripens purple-black*

Teeth
*fine,
sparse*

Leaves
*30 cm,
leathery,
evergreen,
glossy, less shiny,
paler on underside*

From south-eastern Europe, this species is often called 'Laurel' since its foliage resembles Bay laurel or Bay tree (*Laurus nobilis*) whose fragrant leaves, used for wreaths and in cooking, have crinkled margins and are set on shoots that are red above.

Portugal laurel

Prunus lusitanica

Leaves *evergreen, glossy above, dull below*

Petiole *2.5 cm, grooved*

Fruit *1.5 cm on
1 cm pedicels
in stiff, pendent
racemes, irregu-
larly spaced*

Flowers *on
dense 25 cm
spikes*

Flowers
*1.2 cm,
open
mid-June*

Teeth *rounded*

Leaves *to 12 cm, leathery, glabrous.*
Peduncle *ridged behind pedicel*

This evergreen species is native to the Iberian peninsula and while usually a shrubby tree of about 8 m may sometimes reach 16 m. Its buds, leaf stalks and shoots are always green. A form with fewer flowers and wider leaves grows in the Azores.

Cherry plum ● Purple-leaf plum

Prunus cerasifera ● *P. cerasifera* 'Pissardi'

10 m

Flowers *1–5, 2 cm across, borne on previous year's wood and spur shoots, purest white, open with fresh green leaves in March*

Bark *purplish*

Crown *ovoid, more open in type, densely wreathed with small pale pink flowers.* **Leaves** *glossy green.* **Veins** *impressed*

Petiole *1 cm*

Fruit *red or purple.* **Leaves** *downy below, toothed, to 7 cm*

Fruit *2.5 cm, globose*

This attractive tree has an early flowering season, sometimes even in January, or as late as April. The normal green and purple leaf forms are about equally common. Cherry plum is often mistaken for Blackthorn, whose leaves follow its flowers. The edible fruits are not often set in Britain.

Blackthorn

Prunus spinosa

Flowers *single or in pairs, before leaves, 2 cm on a short creamy white 5 mm pedicel, open March–April*

Leaves *4 cm, sharply toothed, downy below with hairs on midrib vein.* **Petiole** *1 cm*

Fruit *1.5 cm, ripen blue to black, bloomed, on short pedicel, fresh green*

Shoot *shiny grey, has terminal thorn.* **Buds** *small.* **Bark** *scaly, thorny*

Leaves *narrow, shape very variable from ovate to obovate, dull green*

Blackthorn or Sloe is a small native suckering shrub or small tree to 6 m. In early spring it is a mass of small creamy-white flowers which obliterate the black of the bark and branches. The fruit ripens in October, and is used to flavour gin.

Plum

Prunus domestica

Shoot *hairy when young, later slightly downy.* **Fruit** *black-purple or red*

Petiole
2.5 cm

Fruit
8 cm, fleshy, sweet, ovoid or ellipsoid, grooved.
Stone *flat with angled sides, free from flesh*

Leaves *to 10 cm, obovate or elliptic, margins with shallow rounded teeth*

Flowers *on last year's wood, single or in pairs, greenish-white, 2 cm*

Leaves *dull above, pubescent on the veins and midrib below*

Plum, a small suckering tree to 10 m, is now thought to be a hybrid between Cherry plum and Blackthorn. Many named varieties are cultivated, and can be grouped into plums and the subsp. *insitia*, which includes the damsons, greengages and Bullace which has downy shoots and rounded fruits.

Apricot

Prunus armenica

Leaves *10 cm, rounded or ovate, base cuneate, margins finely toothed*

Buds
2 mm, single or in pairs

Fruit
3.5 cm, downy, grooved

Petiole *4 cm, red*

Flowers
2.5 cm, white or pink, single, short-stalked

Stone *smooth, free from flesh, margin thickened, ridged*

Apricot makes a small rounded tree to 10 m, and is much cultivated for its delicious orange-red fruit. It does not come from Armenia, as its name suggests, but from northern China. Some cultivars have larger fruit.

Almond

Prunus dulcis

Flowers *appear in March, well before leaves, single or in pairs on a short stalk, bright pink; in older trees they appear only slightly in advance of leaves*

Leaf *usually carries glands at bottom of blade near petiole*

Petiole *2.5 cm*

Leaves *lanceolate, 12 cm, glabrous, finely toothed margins and acuminate tip, "V"-folded near base and along midrib*

Shoot *green or purple.* **Buds** *1–3 cm*

Fruit *7 cm, velvety; hard thin fleshy coat splits to release seed*

Stone, *smooth, pitted*

Almond grows wild, with spiny branches, in its native Mediterranean countries. Its early flowering season has endeared it to gardeners, although it is a short-lived tree with a spreading crown to 10 m. Its nuts are used in confectionery.

Peach

Prunus persica

Leaves *do not have basal glands*

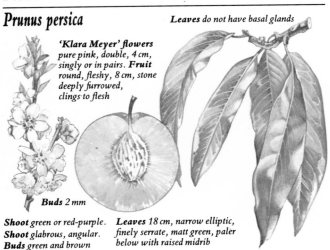

'Klara Meyer' flowers *pure pink, double, 4 cm, singly or in pairs.* **Fruit** *round, fleshy, 8 cm, stone deeply furrowed, clings to flesh*

Buds *2 mm*

Shoot *green or red-purple.* **Shoot** *glabrous, angular.* **Buds** *green and brown*

Leaves *18 cm, narrow elliptic, finely serrate, matt green, paler below with raised midrib*

Peach, which only grows to 8 m, is renowned for its juicy fruit, but is also notable for its single pale rose flowers when in blossom. It was introduced from China in the distant past. Nectarine differs only in having a glabrous fruit.

Legume or Pea family Leguminosae

The Legume or Pea family, comprising several thousand species of trees, shrubs and herbs occurring all over the world, is characterized by pod-like fruits which have a line of seeds along the upper of the two seams. In most familiar species, which belong to the sub-family Lotoideae, the flowers consist of 10 stamens and 5 petals—a "standard" petal covering the top, two wing petals and two "keel" petals.

The second sub-family, the Caesalpinoidae has different flower forms, often with the front two petals enclosing all the others in bud. The Mimosoidae has tiny flowers clustered in heads or on racemes. All genera except *Cercis* have pinnate or bipinnate leaves.

Judas tree

Cercis siliquastrum

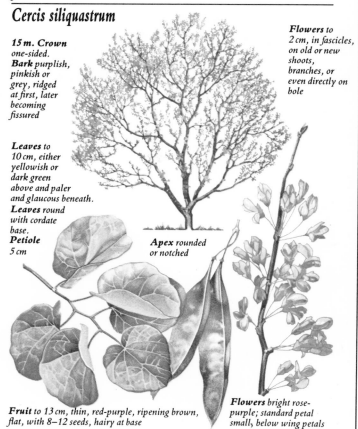

15 m. Crown one-sided.
Bark purplish, pinkish or grey, ridged at first, later becoming fissured

Leaves to 10 cm, either yellowish or dark green above and paler and glaucous beneath.
Leaves round with cordate base.
Petiole 5 cm

Apex rounded or notched

Flowers to 2 cm, in fascicles, on old or new shoots, branches, or even directly on bole

Fruit to 13 cm, thin, red-purple, ripening brown, flat, with 8–12 seeds, hairy at base

Flowers bright rose-purple; standard petal small, below wing petals

Judas tree, not, as commonly supposed, the tree upon which Judas Iscariot hung himself, but named after its native Judea, is unique in the Legume family for its orbicular leaves, similar to Katsura (p 115) but distinguishable by the paired buds. Chinese cercis (*C. racemosa*) is the most distinctive of the six other species, with 30–40 rose-pink flowers in a pendulous raceme.

Robinia

Robinia pseudoacacia

Flowers in racemes up to 20 cm long, fragrant, appear mid to late June

30 m. Crown light, open. **Bole** short, fluted. **Bark** smooth, becoming fissured

Leaf 20 cm, 9–17 leaflets. **Buds** naked, hidden in petiole

Shoot ribbed. **Spines** paired, by most buds

Robinia, also called Black locust or False acacia, is native to the eastern USA. Its fruit pods ripen from green through purple to brown and persist during winter. 'Frisia' has golden leaves.

Honey locust

Gleditsia triacanthos

Shoot slender, often with single or 3-pronged spines. **Lower buds** small, at first hidden in petioles

Bark shallow-ridged with bunches of spines

Bipinnate leaf 20 cm, with 8–14 pinnae of up to 32 2 cm leaflets

Pinnate leaf 10–15 cm, with 14–36 leaflets each 2–4 cm, remotely serrate

This tree often has bipinnate leafs on vigorous shoots and can be distinguished from the closely allied Robinia by its spiny bark, greenish flowers and larger pods. 'Inermis' is often preferred in towns because it lacks spines. 'Sunburst' has rich gold leaves.

Pagoda tree

Sophora japonica

25 m. Crown uneven, low-spreading.
Bark has long, coarse ridges.
Branches very contorted

Shoot
initially
hairy

Leaves 25 cm,
pinnate,
up to 15
leaflets,
whitish
below

Flowers 1.5 cm, in erect,
pubescent 25 cm panicles,
appearing Aug–Sept

The Pagoda tree, although introduced to Europe from Japan, is a
native of China and Korea and differs from Robinia in its pointed,
hairy leaflets and its lack of spines. It produces white, pea-shaped
flowers and pods of up to 8 cm. The Yellow-wood (*Cladrastis
lutea*) has obovate leaflets and a smooth grey bark.

Silver wattle

Acacia dealbata

Leaflets
5 × 1 mm,
finely
haired

Leaves 12 cm, bipinnate.
Pinnae in 10–20 pairs,
each with 30–50 pairs
of linear leaflets

Flowers 3–5 mm across, in panicles of
up to 30 globular heads, appearing Jan

This Australian tree is only hardy in southern Europe and
although grown in sheltered positions farther north, it cannot
survive harsh winters. It rarely exceeds 15 m. Persian acacia
(*Albizia julibrissin*) has larger, deciduous leaves and pink flowers.

147

Voss laburnum

Laburnum x *watereri* 'Vossii'

Bark *smoothish, with columns of buff-brown lenticels*

Leaflets *to 6–8 cm, entire, elliptic or oval with cuneate base, matt above, glaucous and glabrous below, often cupped*

8 m. Crown *spreading on arching, ascending branches*

Leaves *compound, comprising 3 leaflets*

Flowers *2 cm, with 5 petals, 2 upper petals having brown markings*

Shoot *grey-green at first, with adpressed hairs*

Buds *grey-brown, ovoid, with silky white hairs*

Flowers *borne in dense racemes, 25–50 cm long, in late May–June.* **Fruit pods** *4–6 cm, sparsely haired, 1–3 from each raceme.* **Seeds** *toxic*

One of the showiest of small garden trees, this hybrid of Laburnum (*L. anagyroides*) and Scotch laburnum (*L. alpinum*) combines the longer flowers of the former species with the dense racemes of the latter; both differ from Voss in having silky hairs on their leaf undersides. Hop tree (*Ptelea trifoliata*), in the Rutaceae (p152), has similarly compound leaves spotted with oil glands. Its seeds have flat wings like those of elms (pp106–11).

148

Quassia family Simaroubaceae

Tree of heaven

Ailanthus altissima

Bark smooth grey-brown, with shallow cracks

Shoot stout with grey scars

Leaf 60 cm, pinnate. **Leaflets** (13–31) ovate with 1–3 basal teeth, red-stalked, open red

Bud ovoid; terminal absent. **Seed** wings thin, 4 cm

Fruit a samara or key. **Panicles** to 30 cm deep.

Tree of heaven, with a domed crown to 25 metres, comes from north China. It grows rapidly and tolerates pollution, thriving in city streets and parks. Suckering prodigiously, it can produce leaves up to a metre long when such shoots are cut back.

Box family Buxaceae

Box

Buxus sempervirens

Flowers either ♂ or ♀, clustered in leaf axils

10 m. Crown often columnar, leaning. **Bark** cracked into square plates. **Leaf margins** rolled. **Petiole** 1 mm

Leaves 3 cm, leathery, yellowish below. **Fruit** 1 cm, a capsule of 3 segments

Native to some chalky areas of southern England, Box is more common in Mediterranean countries. Its green shoots are square in section and covered in orange hairs while its flowers open in April. It is an ideal tree for hedging and topiary since its small, evergreen leaves are able to withstand repeated clipping. Its hard, heavy wood is much sought-after for engraving.

149

Cashew family Anacardiaceae

Varnish tree

Rhus verniciflua

Leaves to 80 cm

Bark grey, fissured

Bud 1.5 cm. **Leaflets** (7–17) to 20 cm, leathery, downy below

The bark of this Asian tree yields a sap used in making furniture lacquer. Potanin sumach (*R. potanini*) has smaller, coarsely toothed leaves and petioles which can enclose the bud.

Stagshorn sumach

Rhus typhina

Shoot stout, densely covered in short hairs, pithy, has milky sap.
Buds minute, absent as terminals

10 m. Crown low, broad and shrubby. **Bark** thin. **Leaf** 60 cm, has 15–31 leaflets. **Petiole** 8 cm

Leaflets to 12 cm, hairy at first, toothed, magnificent in autumn

Flowers (above) in dense, hairy panicles to 20 cm

Fruit a panicle of densely haired drupes, persistent

The brilliance of its autumn foliage and the curiosity of its crimson "lollipop" fruits remaining well into winter have made this sumach, native to the woods of north-eastern USA, a popular garden tree. Its common name refers to its stout, hairy twigs which resemble the velvety, springtime antlers of stags.

Holly family Aquifoliaceae

Holly

Ilex aquifolium

Shoot grooved

Leaf margins undulate. **Petiole** stout, 1 cm. **Buds** small

♂ (and ♀) **flower** 8 mm, 4-petalled. **Fruit** 6 mm

25 m. Crown pyramidal, dense. **Branches** short. **Bark** smooth. **Leaves** 10 cm, usually prickled but often spineless in crown

'Argenteo-marginata' (♂, right) and **'Golden Queen'** (♂) have variegated leaves. **'Bacciflava'** (♀) has very distinctive berries

Highclere holly • *Ilex x altaclarensis*

'Camelli-folia' cultivar (♀, far left) has leaves with very few prickles. **'Hodginsii'** (♂, left) has broad leaves. **Perny holly** has 3 cm leaves

Holly trees are either male or female and many varied ornamental clones — each with only one sex and each differing in leaf form — have been propagated. Highclere holly is a vigorous hybrid of Holly and Canary holly (*I. perado*) and has large leaves with forward-pointing spines. It, too, has many attractive clones of which 'Hodginsii' is the most common. The Chinese Perny holly (*I. pernyii*) has very small leaves.

Rue family Rutaceae

Korean euodia

Euodia daniellii

Flowers *unisexual, in 15 cm corymbs, opening Sept*

Leaflets *(5–9) 6 cm, cupped, very glossy, obliquely based.* **Margins** *almost entire.* **Veins** *downy below.* **Midribs** *glabrous*

Buds *naked, comprising folded, hairy leaves*

Shoot *and* **rachis** *glabrous*

Leaves *20–25 cm, pinnate.* **Petiole** *3 cm*

This Korean and Chinese species is valuable for the lateness of its flowering. The Amur cork tree (*Phellodendron amurense*), noted for its thick and coarsely ridged corky bark, has larger leaves with 7–13 leaflets and smaller, greyish buds hidden in the leaf stalk.

Spindle family Celastraceae

Spindle tree

Euonymus europaeus

Shoot *rounded, with 4 longitudinal ridges.* **Leaves** *10 cm, glabrous, matt*

Flowers *1 cm, 4-petalled, in cymes of 3–8*

Fruit *15 mm, 4-lobed, deep pink, opening Sept–Oct to reveal orange arils*

6 m. Crown *shrubby*

Native to most of Europe, Spindle is a small tree or shrub renowned for its showy fruit and the attractiveness of its purple-red autumn foliage. Its hard, non-splintering wood was once a useful material for making spindles and other domestic items such as skewers, pegs and knitting needles.

Plane family Platanaceae

While it has few botanical affiliations with the Aceraceae (pp 154–65), the leaves of this family were once mistaken for those of maples. This is reflected in the specific names of two maples — *platanoides* (p154) and *pseudoplatanus* (p155) — and in that of *Platanus acerifolia*. Planes, however, always have *alternate* leaves.

Oriental plane

Platanus orientalis

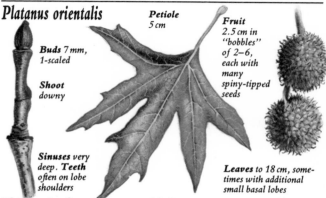

Petiole 5 cm

Fruit 2.5 cm in "bobbles" of 2–6, each with many spiny-tipped seeds

Buds 7 mm, 1-scaled

Shoot downy

Sinuses very deep. **Teeth** often on lobe shoulders

Leaves to 18 cm, sometimes with additional small basal lobes

This species from the eastern Mediterranean can grow 30 metres high and is used as a shade tree in many southern European villages. Its shortish bole can achieve a girth as large as 13 metres.

London plane

Platanus x acerifolia

Lobing very variable

Leaf base variable

45 m. Crown high; domed

Branches large, mostly ascending. **Bark** flakes to give a dappled effect

Leaves to 20 cm but very variable; downy initially but soon glossy, glabrous except on veins below. **Petiole** 5 cm, has enlarged base hiding bud

A majestic habit, an immunity to urban atmospheres and a resistance to barbaric and unsightly pollarding have countributed to this tree's popularity and its success was confirmed last century when it became widely planted in London streets. It is a hybrid of *P. orientalis* and American plane (*P. occidentalis*) which has more shallowly lobed leaves and single, rarely paired, fruit.

Maple family Aceraceae

Maples are noted for the rich autumnal tints of their leaves which are usually palmately lobed and always set in opposite pairs. Small green or yellow flowers appear in corymbs, racemes or panicles and are normally bisexual. Distinctive samaras (fruit keys) consist of paired seeds (nutlets) set in flat, membranous wings to facilitate wind dispersal.

Norway maple
Acer platanoides

Flowers open early Apr, before lvs in erect corymbs of 20–30 **Petals** 8 mm wide. **Buds** 1 cm tall, red-purple. **Shoot** stout, hairless, dark brown

25 m. **Crown** broad-domed, densely leaved. **Bole** short. **Bark** grey-brown, finely ridged

Leaf 12 × 15 cm, cordate. 2–6 coarse teeth per lobe, edges of central lobes parallel. **Blade** uns paler. **Leaf stalk** long, 15 cm, with milky sap distinguishing it from similar maples

Samara nutlets flat. **Wings** each 3–5 cm, almost horizontal

'Schwedleri' opens pink-red. Green by summer, then purple in autumn

'Drummondii' cv has small leaves with white or cream variegation

Native to northern and central Europe, the Norway maple is most attractive in April when its flowers open and in autumn when its foliage turns deep yellow. This tree is suited to urban sites and a wide range of cultivars is available: 'Crimson King' has deep red-purplish leaves throughout summer.

154

Acer pseudoplatanus

Shoot green-brown. **Buds** ovoid, 1 cm, green, red margins. **Flowers** 50–100, hanging in dense, 12 cm panicles

Samara wings each 3 cm, set at 90°

35 m. Crown broad. **Branches** billow. **Bark** scaly, light grey-brown; silver, smooth on young trees. Sycamores often grown for hard, close-grained timber and to act as windbreaks

Leaf to 18 × 26 cm on young trees, more often 15 × 20 cm. 5 lobes, more rarely 3–7. **Teeth** coarse. **Blade** underside glaucous. **Veins** net-like. **Leaf stalk** reddish

'*Erectum*' cultivar (1) has fastigiate brs. Lvs of '*Purpureum*' (2) are matt green with purple undersides

'*Brilliantissimum*' leaf (1) opens shrimp-pink, turning through yellow to dark green. '*Leopoldii*' (2) can have leaves stained yellowish-pink. '*Worleei*' cv leaf (3) opens in gold and yellow, fading to green-yellow

A wide tolerance of different sites and a facility to germinate, which can make it a rapacious weed, have enabled the Sycamore to colonize most of Britain. Van Volxem maple (*A. velutinum*) has larger leaves and upright flower panicles. Devil's horn maple (*A. diabolicum*) has ciliate, pubescently veined leaves.

Field maple

Acer campestre

Buds *5 mm, apex hairy.* **Winter shoot** *often glossy*

Leaf stalk *slender 5–9 cm, with milky sap*

Samaras *in c. 4 pairs, hairy.* **Wings** *each 3 cm at 180°, brown when ripe*

Leaf *4–7 cm, 5-lobed with basal pair small or absent, sinuses acute.* **Blade** *paler below, gold in autumn.* **Vein axils** *hairy.* **Margins** *ciliate.*

Bark *grey, cracked and fissured*

Field maple is a common hedgerow tree throughout Europe and the only maple native to Britain, where it is common in the south. The Miyabe maple (*A. miyabei*), from Japan, has larger, paler leaves cut less than halfway to the leaf base and a leaf stalk which clasps the shoot very strongly, almost hiding the bud.

Italian maple

Acer opalus

Flowers *appear in April before lvs, in pendulous corymbs.* **Fruit** *in bunches 8–16.* **Wings** *each 2.5 cm, acutely angled*

Winter twig *glabrous with pale lenticels*

Leaf *12 cm, 3- or 5-lobed.* **Teeth** *coarse, irregular.* **Veins** *impressed.* **Blade** *underside glaucous, hairy.* **Leaf stalk** *10 cm with watery sap*

Italian maple, also found in France and Spain, is a small tree reaching 15 m. Heldreich maple (*A. heldreichii*) has deep, narrow leaf sinuses—Trauvetter's maple (*A. trauvetteri*) has deep, wide ones. Both these species have *erect* flower panicles.

Caucasian maple

Acer cappadocium

Leaf *8 × 12 cm, cordate.*
Lobes *acuminately tipped.*
Blade *paler below.* **Vein
axils** *tufted.* **Sinuses**
shallow, obtuse. **Young
leaves** *reddish.* **Autumn
foliage** *golden yellow*

12 m. Crown
dense, domed.
Bark *smooth,
fawn-grey.*
Bole *short.
Only maple
producing
suckers*

Fruit *in pendulous corymbs.*
Wings *each 7 cm, spread
widely.* **Leaf stalk** *to 12 cm,
with milky sap*

Native to an area stretching from Asia Minor across the Himalayas to China, Caucasian maple has a particularly beautiful, golden autumn colour. Its cultivar 'Aurum' has pale yellow-green leaves while those of 'Rubrum' have their new growth tinged deep red. Thunberg maple (*A. mono*) has similar leaves but is recognizable by its grey-brown shoots.

Lobel maple

Acer lobelii

Leaf *12 cm, 3–5 lobed.*
Margins *crinkled.* **Blade**
dull, paler below.
Vein axils *tufted*

**Leaf lobe
tip** *twists
upwards or
sideways*

Leaf stalk
10 cm, green.
Sap *milky*

25 m. Crown *columnar, broadening.*
Shoot *green or purplish with initial
bloom of glaucous white wax*

With similarly lobed, toothless leaves and shoots which stay green for several years, Lobel maple can easily be confused with *A. cappadocium* but is ultimately differentiated from it by the twisted tips and wrinkled margins of its leaves. It grows wild in the mountain woodlands of southern Italy.

Oregon maple

Acer macrophyllum

Shoot *stout, green.*
Buds *stout, conic with red-brown scales*

Leaf sinus *deep, acute, rounded*

Leaf blade *very large, 20 × 35 cm, 5-lobed, thin-textured.* **Teeth** *blunt.* **Margins** *ciliate*

Leaf *paler below.* **Leaf stalk** *long, 15–35 cm, red or green, clasps stem closely, almost hiding bud.* **Samaras** *big, each wing 5 cm at 90° or less*

Flower panicles *narrow, 25 cm*

This North American West Coast species grows quickly into a majestic tree of about 30 m with a tall, domed crown of ascending, arched branches. Oregon is the only maple with both milky sap *and* hanging panicles and its large leaves and clasping leaf stalks will readily confirm this identification.

Sugar maple

Acer saccharum

Samara wings *2–2.5 cm, ripening brown*

30 m. Crown *open.* **Bark** *smooth grey, later fissured into plates*

Leaf *12 × 18 cm, 5-lobed, fresh green, gold or scarlet in autumn.* **Teeth** *rounded, triangular, 3–5 on 3 main lobes.* **Sinuses** *deep, rounded.* **Buds** *6 mm, brown, ovoid-conic, hairy*

In its native range stretching from eastern Canada to Texas, this is the tree tapped for maple syrup. Its leaf is not dissimilar to that of Norway maple (p 154) but has a watery sap. Black maple (*A. nigrum*) has darker, duller, yellow-veined leaves which are cupped and three-lobed. Its bark is ridged.

158

Silver maple

Acer saccharinum

Leaf stalk pink, 12 cm, slender

Shoot red-brown then purple. **Buds** long, 1 cm when terminal

Leaf 15 cm, cordate, 5-lobed, main side-lobes at 45°, all with lobules

Blade undersides pubescent.

Samaras on 3–5 cm stalks **Wings** 5 cm, twisted, broad tipped

Silver maple is native to eastern North America south of Quebec and grows to some 30 m with a tall, raggedly domed crown and a smooth, silvery bark. In early March its maroon flowers, opening before the leaves, enliven the tree; in autumn its foliage assumes spectacular hues of yellow, gold or red.

Red maple

Acer rubrum

Veins red, **Blade colours** intensify during September

30 m. Crown tall, domed, fast growing. **Bark** smooth, silver-grey, finally darker, scaling

Leaves 11 cm, usually dark green, glossy above, silvery below

Flowers in dense clusters, opening March, before leaves

Shoot red-brown or maroon, slender. **Buds** very small, 3 mm, ciliate on scales red-brown, pointed

This North American tree is aptly named since its flowers, fruits, shoots and autumn tints are all red or reddish; its leaf undersides and bark are silver. It is closely related to Silver maple, often growing near it, but has smaller, less deeply lobed leaves.

Japanese maple

Acer palmatum

15 m. Crown *tall, domed.* **Bole** *short.* **Bark** *smooth, brown.* **Shoot** *green or purple, without lenticels.* **Buds** *small, 3 mm, red or green, surrounded by minute bristles.* **Samaras** *small, 2 cm across.* **Wings** *set at obtuse angles*

Flowers *6–8 mm wide, in erect panicles of 12–15, on 4 cm pedicels*

Leaves *9 cm, shiny and light green below.* **Lobes** *deeply cut.* **Teeth** *paired.* **Leaf stalks** *3–5 cm*

*'**Dissectum**' leaves have 7–11 lobes cut so deeply that some forms have leaves totally palmate*

*'**Senkaki**' or Coral-bark maple, tall, fast growing. Shoot coral red in winter. Leaves become orange-yellow in autumn*

*'**Atropurpureum**' leaves 5-lobed, reddish purple. Brighter in autumn*

Japanese maple is a small, bushy tree. While its leaves turn brilliant shades in autumn, it can be equally attractive in spring, when its purple flowers contrast strongly with its fresh green leaves. Of the enormous range of its cultivars, the most spectacular is 'Senkaki' and the most popular, 'Atropurpureum'. Oliver maple (*A. oliveranum*), from central China, has stiffer and glossier leaves which are five-lobed and minutely serrate. Their undersides are often pubescent.

160

Full-moon maple

Acer japonicum

Leaves 13 cm, bases cordate. Lobes 7–11, coarsely toothed, cut shallowly. Veins hairy below. Autumn leaves (below) especially fine while turning

Fruit wings each 2.5–3 cm

This native of Japan derives its name from its orbicular leaves. It is represented in gardens by two clones: 'Vitifolium' is larger, with leaves up to 15 cm offering fine autumn colour; 'Aureum' is smaller and has golden yellow foliage throughout summer.

David maple

Acer davidii

Margins unevenly serrate. Veins parallel, main one red with minute axil tufts

Leaf blades ovate with pointed tips but very varied as 'George Forrest' (above), 'Ernest Wilson' (left).

Bark olive green with white or green "snaking" stripes. Branches ascend steeply. Shoot maroon or dark green-red, later striped white. Buds 1 cm

This is the most common of the snake-bark maples, which have distinctive barks with white or greenish stripes and flowers in long, dense racemes. It has a wide natural distribution in China and as a species is extremely variable. One form, 'Ernest Wilson', has a lower, rounded habit and yellower, narrower leaves folded at the base of their main vein.

Kyushu maple

Acer capilles

Teeth shallow, uneven, crenate

Leaves 15 × 11 cm, rounded at base, glossy above, paler below. **Veins** very impressed, parallel, with small, yellow axil "pegs" along main vein

Bark very distinctive, enduring well on old trees

Samaras small, each wing 1.5 cm, set at obtuse angles, red when ripe, numerous on older trees

15 m. Crown spreads. **Bole** short. **Branches** ascend, then arch out

This Japanese maple is the only snake-bark whose leaves have small forward-pointing side lobes, impressed veins and yellowish axil "pegs". Its autumn colours and red shoots and buds give it the alternative name of "Red snake-bark maple".

Moosewood

Acer pensylvanicum

Leaves to 20 cm, red in autumn, very variable in size and shape but always cordate with rounded sinuses

Leaf stalk stout and long, 12 cm, grooved

Teeth sharp and uneven. **Sinuses** shallow. **Veins** have red hairs below

Fruit 5 cm across, bunched, abundant. **Wings** curved, widely set

Moosewood, from eastern North America, is the only snake-bark not indigenous to eastern Asia. Honshu maple (*A. rufinerve*), from Japan, has smaller leaves with rufous, pubescent veins, buds bloomed white and small, round nutlets. Hers' maple (*A. hersii*) has matt leaves, larger fruit and no red colouring.

Montpelier maple

Acer monspessulanum

Buds *small, 3 mm, ovoid.*
Shoot *slender, slightly glossy.* **Flowers** *open in June (with or before leaves) in small, erect panicles that are 5 cm wide*

Samara
wings small, each 1.2 cm, set almost parallel or overlapping

Leaf *4 × 7 cm, cordate, usually entire.* **Blade underside** *glaucous with some axil tufts near base.* **Leaf stalk** *4 cm, slender, pink*

This maple has a wide natural range from Mediterranean Spain and north Africa to Iran and is often used for hedging, very rarely reaching its maximum height of 15 m. Cretan maple (*A. sempervirens*) is almost evergreen and has small, stiff, variable leaves, which may be unlobed or have three rounded lobes.

Amur maple

Acer ginnala

Flowers
in erect showy panicles of c. 50, opening in late May

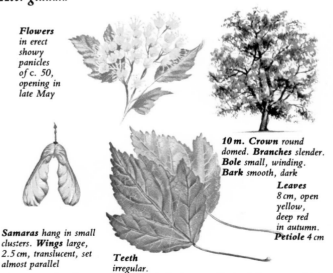

10 m. **Crown** *round domed.* **Branches** *slender.* **Bole** *small, winding.* **Bark** *smooth, dark*

Leaves
8 cm, open yellow, deep red in autumn. **Petiole** *4 cm*

Samaras *hang in small clusters.* **Wings** *large, 2.5 cm, translucent, set almost parallel*

Teeth
irregular.

Amur maple, from north-east Asia, is a small shrubby tree which shows its early autumn crimson for a brief period in September. Trident maple (*A. buergeranum*) has three-lobed leaves, the lobes pointing directly forwards in the manner of Neptune's trident. These leaves have silvery undersides.

Paperbark maple

Acer griseum

Leaves trifoliate. **Leaflets** 4 × 10 cm, opening reddish, becoming yellow before normal green. **Teeth** big

Petioles 5 cm, hairy. **Veins** impressed, midribs coarsely haired. **Fruit** in 3 pairs with large, forward-pointing wings and hairy nutlets

Bark red or coppery brown, flaking from both bole and branches

15 m. Crown slender, open. **Branches** winding. **Foliage** shades of red and orange in autumn

Paperbark maple, from central China, is planted for its exquisite but fleeting autumn tints and the permanent beauty of its bark. Chosen maple (*A. triflorum*), whose name derives from the Japanese for Korea, has a rough, grey-brown bark. Rock maple (*A. pentaphyllum*) has digitate leaves, glaucous beneath.

Nikko maple

Acer nikoense

Leaflet undersides pubescent. **Leaf stalks** 7 cm, thick, densely haired. **Samara wings** in 3 pairs, broad, 2.5 cm long, glabrous, set at angle of 90° or more. **Nutlets** very hairy

Leaves trifoliate, opening in April. **Leaflets** 10 × 3.5 cm, leathery; side ones subsessile, obliquely based. **Teeth** very small

Bark smooth, initially grey with greenish tinge, becoming pink-grey with fine red speckles

Nikko maple, native to Japan and central China, has lively autumn foliage although its bark cannot compare with that of Paperback maple. Manchurian maple (*A. mandschuricum*) has a similar bark to Nikko but saw-toothed leaves with long stalks.

Box elder

Acer negundo

Leaves *bright light green with no autumn colour,* **Leaflets** *5–7, sometimes 3 irregularly toothed.* **Leaf stalk** *8 cm, pink or yellow*

Shoot *green, later bloomed violet*

♂ **flowers** *set in pendulous clusters of 12–16*

Samaras *in racemes, ripen early, remain after leaf fall.* **Wings** *2 cm, set acutely, incurved*

Possibly overplanted, Box elder rarely produces a fine specimen; its cultivar 'Variegatum' produces both fruit and leaves that are variegated white. Henry maple (*A. henryi*) is a Chinese species with red autumn foliage, pink-red leaf stalks and bright green, glossy shoots.

Pittosporum family Pittosporaceae

Pittosporum

Pittosporum tenuifolium

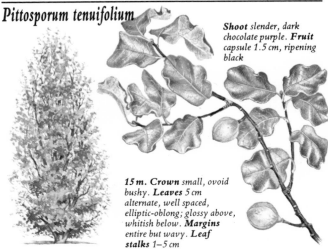

Shoot *slender, dark chocolate purple.* **Fruit** *capsule 1.5 cm, ripening black*

15 m. Crown *small, ovoid bushy.* **Leaves** *5 cm alternate, well spaced, elliptic-oblong; glossy above, whitish below.* **Margins** *entire but wavy.* **Leaf stalks** *1–5 cm*

The pittosporum family comes mainly from Australasia, south-east Asia and South Africa although one species is native to Madeira. Pittosporum itself is native to both islands of New Zealand and is noticeable for its fragrant flowers.

165

Horse chestnut family Hippocastanaceae

This small family, named after the resemblance of its fruit to that of *Castanea* (p105), is dominated by the *Aesculus* genus. Opposite, digitately compound leaves, showy and erect flower panicles and large "conker" seeds are identifying features.

Horse chestnut

Aesculus hippocastanum

Flowers numerous, up to 150 on 15–30 cm panicles. **Petals** (5) have basal blotches

40 m. Crown tall, spreading, dense. **Branches** upswept, sometimes layering

Buds 2.5 cm. **Shoot** stout. **Leaf scars** horseshoe shaped

Leaflets (5–7) 10–25 cm, sessile, unevenly serrate

Fruit 5 cm

This species provides the ammunition for conkers which was once played with snail shells (conches). Japanese horse chestnut (*A. turbinata*) also has sticky buds *and* sessile leaflets but the latter are evenly toothed and can be up to 40 cm long.

Red horse chestnut

Aesculus x carnea

Buds not sticky. **Flowers** in 12–20 cm panicles, opening May; 'Briottii' flowers are deeper red

Bark similar to Horse chestnut but rougher. **Bole** often cankered

This hybrid is smaller than its Horse chestnut parent while its buds resemble those of its other parent, the American Red buckeye (*A. pavia*) which has the same red inflorescences.

Indian horse chestnut

Aesculus indica

Leaflets (5–9) 15–30 cm, stalked, finely serrate, opening glossy yellow. **Flowers** in slender, 30 cm panicles. **Bark** smooth

Fruit smooth. **Seed** 4 cm with pale hilum

Leaflet undersides glabrous and glaucous. **Bud** small, 1.5 cm, sticky. **Petiole** 18 cm. **Shoot** rough

This majestic native of the Himalayas flowers and fruits 6 weeks after *A. hippocastanum* and is the most common of those *Aesculus* species with 4-petalled flowers and resinous buds. Another is California buckeye (*A. californica*) which has pear-shaped fruit, smaller, sessile leaflets and flat petioles.

Yellow buckeye

Aesculus flava

20 m. Crown narrow with fine autumn yellows and orange-reds. **Branches** small, pendulous and twisting. **Bole** straight. **Bark** grey- or red-brown, smooth becoming scaly

Leaves have 5–7 leaflets with impressed veins. **Flowers** 4 cm, dense, sometimes pink, on 10–15 cm panicles. **Petals** (4) forward-pointing

Leaflet margins finely serrate

Leaflet 15 cm, glabrous, sometimes downy below, on 1.5 cm stalk. **Fruit** 6 cm, smooth, 2-seeded

Buckeyes, whose name arose when their hila (pale, basal seed scars) were likened to the eyes of deer, are native to the eastern USA. They have non-sticky buds. Yellow buckeye presents the best of their autumn tints. The doubly serrate leaves of Sunrise buckeye (*A. neglecta* 'Erythroblastos') open pink-red.

Lime family Tiliaceae

Limes have large, toothed, heart-shaped leaves, flowers that hang in cymes and large distinctive bracts attached for half their length to the flower stalk. The fruit is dry and nutty.

Large-leaved lime

Tilia platyphyllos

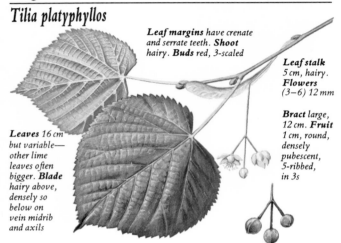

Leaf margins *have crenate and serrate teeth.* **Shoot** *hairy.* **Buds** *red, 3-scaled*

Leaf stalk *5 cm, hairy.* **Flowers** *(3–6) 12 mm*

Bract *large, 12 cm.* **Fruit** *1 cm, round, densely pubescent, 5-ribbed, in 3s*

Leaves *16 cm but variable— other lime leaves often bigger.* **Blade** *hairy above, densely so below on vein midrib and axils*

The Large-leaved lime is native to most of Europe (including parts of Britain) and has a narrow crown with branches that ascend steeply. Its bark is grey and fissured; shoots at the foot of the bole are rare. American lime (*T. americana*) has larger leaves which are coarsely toothed, almost glabrous and paler below.

Small-leaved lime

Tilia cordata

Foliage *dense, slightly pendent.* **Leaves** *6 cm.* **Margins** *finely serrate.* **Blades** *roundish, cordate, acuminate, shiny above, glaucous below.* **Axil tufts** *prominent, orange-brown*

30 m. Crown *narrow, very twiggy in winter.* **Bole** *can be burred*

Winter shoot *glossy brown with light lenticels.* **Buds** *have 2 visible scales*

This species of lime is recognizable by the size of its roundish leaves and its flowers, which spread irregularly and do not hang. Mongolian lime (*T. mongolica*) is often planted where a smaller tree is required. Its leaves have large, coarse, triangular teeth which almost become lobes.

European lime

Tilia x europaea

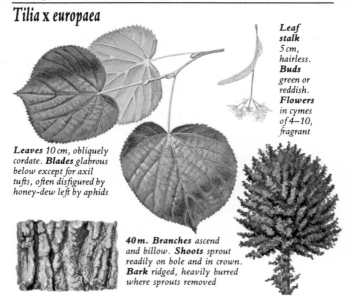

Leaf stalk *5 cm, hairless.* **Buds** *green or reddish.* **Flowers** *in cymes of 4–10, fragrant*

Leaves *10 cm, obliquely cordate.* **Blades** *glabrous below except for axil tufts, often disfigured by honey-dew left by aphids*

40 m. Branches *ascend and billow.* **Shoots** *sprout readily on bole and in crown.* **Bark** *ridged, heavily burred where sprouts removed*

Often the largest broadleaf in an area, the European lime is a natural hybrid of the Large- and Small-leaved species and its apparent ubiquity as a park and street tree has been attributed to seventeenth-century Dutch horticulturists who found it more easy to propagate than its parents. It is often pollarded.

Caucasian lime

Tilia x euchlora

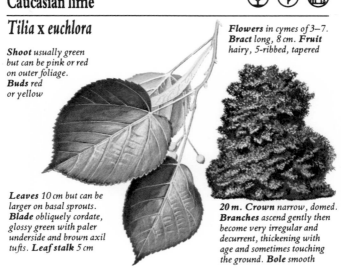

Shoot *usually green but can be pink or red on outer foliage.* **Buds** *red or yellow*

Flowers *in cymes of 3–7.* **Bract** *long, 8 cm.* **Fruit** *hairy, 5-ribbed, tapered*

Leaves *10 cm but can be larger on basal sprouts.* **Blade** *obliquely cordate, glossy green with paler underside and brown axil tufts.* **Leaf stalk** *5 cm*

20 m. Crown *narrow, domed.* **Branches** *ascend gently then become very irregular and decurrent, thickening with age and sometimes touching the ground.* **Bole** *smooth*

Caucasian lime has uncertain origins and may be a cross between the Small-leaved lime and the rare *T. dasystyla*, also from the Caucasus. Its agreeable foliage and immunity to aphids make it more suitable for streets than European lime although its lower branches eventually become far too decurrent for such sites.

169

Silver lime

Tilia tomentosa

Leaf blades *12 × 10 cm, rounded, obliquely cordate, densely pubescent below.* **Buds** *6–8 mm.* **Shoot** *remains pubescent*

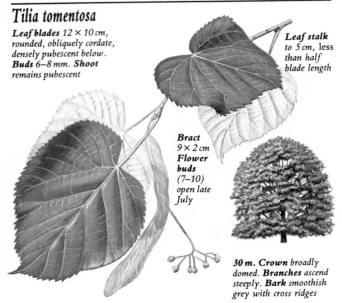

Leaf stalk *to 5 cm, less than half blade length*

Bract *9 × 2 cm* **Flower buds** *(7–10) open late July*

30 m. Crown *broadly domed.* **Branches** *ascend steeply.* **Bark** *smoothish grey with cross ridges*

Silver lime displays an attractive habit, especially when its pubescent leaves are ruffled by wind. It is a native of the Balkans. Oliver lime (*T. oliveri*), from China, has larger, evenly cordate leaves and glabrous leaves.

Pendent silver lime

Tilia petiolaris

30 m. Crown *dense, narrow.* **Branchlets** *pendent.* **Bark** *has shallow ridges*

Leaf blade *to 12 cm, very cordate, serrate, densely pubescent below.* **Petiole** *more than half blade length*

Usually grafted on to *T. europaea* (p 169), producing an unsightly change in bark texture at a height of some 2 m, this tree hybridizes with *T. americana* (p 168) to produce Von Moltke lime (*T. x moltkei*) whose larger leaves are lightly pubescent below.

Soapberry family Sapindaceae

Pride of India

Koelreuteria paniculata

Leaf huge, 20–40 cm, pinnate with 11–13 leaflets or bipinnate. *Leaflets* 3–8 cm, coarsely toothed, paler below. *Leaf stalk* grooved above. *Shoot* irregular. *Buds* small, 3 mm

Veins pubescent below

Flowers 1 cm, in large panicles

A native of Japan and China, this tree has few associations with India. It reaches a maximum height of 15 m, has a widespreading crown and is distinguished by its decurrent leaflets, showy flowers and bladder-like fruit. It turns yellow in autumn.

Euchryphia family Eucryphiaceae

Nymans eucryphia

Eucryphia x *nymansensis* 'Nymansay'

Flowers large, 8 cm across.

Stamens numerous. *Petals* (4 or 5) open late August to mid-Sept. *Shoot* 4-ribbed, pubescent

Leaves mostly trifoliate. *Leaflets* to 8 cm, leathery, shiny, crenately toothed. *Leaf stalk* 2 cm, pubescent

An attractive, columnar evergreen and the more valuable for being late-flowering, this tree is a cross between two Chilean species of eucryphia. Rostrevor eucryphia (*E.* x *intermedia*) has smaller flowers and darker leaves that·are glaucous below.

Tea family Theaceae

Deciduous camellia

Stewartia pseudocamellia

Buds 5 mm, shiny

Flowers 6 cm across, cup-shaped, on 1 cm pedicel

Veins impressed

Leaves 9 cm, dull above, shiny and silky-haired below

Shoot glabrous, slender

Bark brown with purple-grey scales; orange where flaking has occurred

Deciduous camellia, a small, slender tree to 15 m, is noted for its attractive flowers, which remain in bloom over several weeks from July, and the brilliant colours of its autumn leaves. Chinese stewartia (*S. sinensis*) has a creamy white or pinkish bark.

Tupelo family Nyssaceae

Tupelo

Nyssa sylvatica

Shoot smooth, hairless, with small lenticels. **Buds** 5 mm, conic

Leaves 5–12 cm, entire, glossy above, paler below. **Petiole** 1 cm. **Fruit** 1 cm, oval, in pairs on 4 cm peduncle

25 m. Crown conic. **Bark** grey, fissured

The genus *Nyssa* comprises four species: three from eastern USA and one from China. Tupelo is the only common one, remaining a dull tree for most of the year until early autumn when it becomes a blaze of glossy scarlet, gold, and finally red.

Davidia family Davidaceae

Dove tree

Davidia involucrata

Flower 2 cm wide

20 m. Crown domed. **Bole** short. **Branches** radiate outwards. **Bark** purplish, flaking brown, with vertical fissures

Bracts large, to 17 cm, in uneven pairs, paper-thin

Lenticels pale

Buds 1.5 cm, conic, shiny

Leaves 15 cm, shiny above, softly hairy below. **Veins** impressed. **Petiole** 15 cm. **Vilmoriniana leaf** (below): 20 cm, coarsely serrate, glabrous below

Shoot glabrous

Fruit 3 cm, hard, fleshy, ribbed, ripening purple, with prominent lenticels. **Pedicel** 10 cm

Dedicated to its discoverer, Père David, this is a vigorous, lime-like tree native only to western China. Its appearance in May can be very striking, when the large, white bracts which subtend each flower drape the branches and give the tree its name. *D. involucrata* var. *vilminiana* has larger leaves and is more frequent than the type.

173

Myrtle family Myrtaceae

Cider gum

Eucalyptus gunnii

Adult leaves 10 cm, stalked, alternate

Juvenile leaves sessile, opposite

Fruit in 3s, 6 mm

35 m. Crown conic, with wispy halo when growing fast. **Bark** peels in orangey strips to expose smooth grey surface below

Cider gum – so called as a cider can be made from the sap – is the hardest gum. It is a native of Tasmania and coppices readily if cut back. The flowers before opening are covered by a cap (operculum) of fused petals.

Snow gum

Eucalyptus niphophila

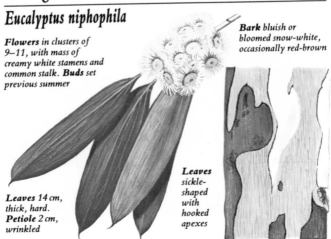

Flowers in clusters of 9–11, with mass of creamy white stamens and common stalk. **Buds** set previous summer

Bark bluish or bloomed snow-white, occasionally red-brown

Leaves sickle-shaped with hooked apexes

Leaves 14 cm, thick, hard. **Petiole** 2 cm, wrinkled

A small tree reaching 10 m, Snow gum grows wild in south-eastern Australia at heights up to 2,000 m above sea-level. Blue gum (*E. globulus*), from Tasmania, has much larger leaves, glaucous blue when juvenile.

174

Ivy family Araliaceae

Ivy

Hedera helix

Fruit *6 mm, ripens black in late autumn to winter*

Flowers *a cluster of globose umbels, appear October, attract moths*

Vegetative shoots *twist and climb any support*

Adult leaves *unlobed, shiny*

Stem *bristly with supporting, not feeding, roots*

Juvenile leaves *3- or 5-lobed*

Ivy is a plant which climbs to reach sunlight, but can easily be mistaken for a tree when its prolific growth and flowers blanket its host, which probably suffers no harm. It ceases climbing and flowers once the leaves are exposed to full light.

Prickly castor oil tree

Kalopanax pictus var. maximowiczii

Leaves *20 cm with 5–7 lobes.* **Margins** *serrate*

Leaves *open red.* **Veins** *strong*

15 m. Crown *gaunt.* **Branches** *spaced.* **Leader** *often leans*

Petiole *20 cm, with bulbous base*

Shoot *stout with fleshy spines.* **Buds** *4 cm, conic*

Bark *dull with crossing ridges*

Kalopanax is an unusual Asian genus comprising only one species. The variety shown here is the commonest but the type which has smaller leaves with shallower lobes is also occasionally seen. White flowers are carried in heads up to 60 cm across.

Dogwood family Cornaceae

Table dogwood

Cornus controversa

15 m. Branches *in tiers.*
Bark *grey, smooth,*
becoming cross-ridged.
Shoot *dark red,*
glabrous

Petiole
4 cm

Flowers *each 1.5 cm,*
in upright cymes, June-July

Leaves
hairy below

Leaves *12 cm, shiny, alternate; those of 'Variegata'*
narrower, creamy yellow and green, twisted

Table dogwood is a wide-ranging tree, extending from the Himalayas to Japan. Like all dogwoods it has leaves with basal veins curving parallel to the margin but, apart from one American species, *C. alternifolia*, is unique in its alternative leaves.

Nuttall dogwood

Cornus nuttallii

10 m. Crown *conic, open*

Leaves *12 cm, hairy both*
sides, red below in
autumn. **Petiole** *1 cm*

Fruit *a*
cluster of
red drupes.
Flower
buds *set*
in autumn

Flowers *green, small*

Branches *whorl.* **Bark**
smooth, becoming scaly

Flower bracts *large,*
5–8 cm, creamy, pointed,
opening May (or some-
times October)

Presenting a magnificent display when the conspicuous bracts of its flower-heads open, Nuttall dogwood is a native of the North American west coast where it reaches 30 m. Flowering dogwood (*C. florida*) has smaller leaves and always has four bracts.

Japanese dogwood

Cornus kousa

Leaves *8 cm, variable, entire, soon glabrous except for axil tufts, glaucous below.* **Petiole** *5 mm.* **Shoot** *glabrous*

Flowers *appear in dense mass in May-June.* **Bracts** *5 cm, pointed, set around flowers*

Fruit *sweet, strawberry-like, of many fleshy drupes, ripening late summer*

Leaf margins *entire*

Flower bracts *star-like*

Flowers *held upright above shoots*

This dogwood is native to Japan and central China and grows to 10 m. Its branches are somewhat tiered like those of Table dogwood, from which it can be distinguished by its opposite leaves. It is notable for its brilliant autumn reds.

Cornelian cherry

Cornus mas

Leaves *10 cm, variable, shiny above, with adpressed hairs on both sides.* **Veins** *forward-curved.* **Petiole** *2 cm*

Bark *scaly*

10 m. Crown *spreading on several main stems*

Flowers *in clusters 2.5 cm wide*

Fruit *1.5 cm.* **Pedicel** *1 cm*

Bud scales *valvate*

Flowers *appear before leaves*

Flowers *4 mm, with 4 bracts at cluster base*

This ornamental is a native of southern Europe and has long been cultivated for the bright yellow flowers which cloak its bare branches in February and March and for its abundant fruit which provides another attractive display in October. This fruit is edible and can be made into jam or syrup.

Heather family Ericaceae

Strawberry tree

Arbutus unedo

Petiole
7 mm,
hairy.
Shoot
long-
haired

Leaves 10 cm, variable,
serrate, shiny, very dark
above, paler below

Flowers
6 mm, pink
or white

Panicles of
15–20
flowers
open in
Oct–Dec

Fruit 2 cm, warty, green-
yellow, ripening to orange-
pink as new flowers open

Native to south-west Ireland and southern Europe, the Strawberry tree is a small evergreen up to 10 m high and has a dark red-brown, finely fissured bark. Its strawberry-like fruit takes a year to ripen. It can be eaten but its insipidness is indicated by the tree's specific name *unedo* meaning "I eat (only) one."

Madrona

Arbutus menziensii

Leaves to
14 cm,
glossy
above, very
glaucous
below

Leaves
leathery

Petiole
3 cm

Bark smooth, peeling,
cracked at base

Shoot green,
later orange

Flowers 3 mm,
open April–
May in 20 cm
panicles

Fruit 13 mm,
a warty globular berry
that ripens in late summer

Madrona is native to the Pacific coast of North America where it attains 40 m and is readily identified by its bark. Similar barks are carried by the Greek strawberry tree (*A. andrachne*) which has narrower leaves and *A.* x *andrachnoides* with serrate leaves.

Sorrel tree

Oxydendrum arboreum

Flowers 1 cm, in panicles to 25 cm

Teeth *fine*

Leaves *18 cm, thin, glossy above, pale and dull below, red in autumn*

Branches *twisted*

15 m. Crown *narrow and domed*

Shoot *green below.* **Buds** *2 mm*

Petiole *1.5 cm.* **Shoot** *glabrous*

Bole *long, straight*

Native to the eastern USA, Sorrel is unusual in flowering in autumn, its foliage often turning scarlet while it is still in flower. Its name refers to the pleasantly sour taste of its leaves. The fruit capsules are whitish and 12 mm wide.

Ebony family Ebenaceae

Persimmon

Diospyros virginiana

Flowers 2 cm, open in July

Leaves *dark glossy above*

Bark *black or dark grey, cracked into squares*

Fruit *4 cm, orange or purple.* **Calyx** *4-lobed, persistent*

Leaves *to 15 cm, waved, paler below*

Shoot *slender, downy or glabrous.* **Buds** *small*

Persimmon, from the south-eastern USA, grows up to 20 m and is distinguished by its glossy leaves, its hanging, urn-shaped flowers and its astringent fruit which is edible after exposure to autumn frosts. Date plum (*D. lotus*), an Asian relative, has petioles only 1 cm long and flowers 8 mm white.

Storax family Styracaceae

Snowbell tree

Styrax japonica

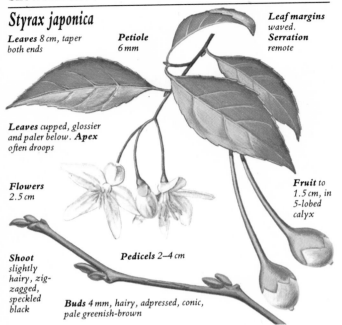

Leaves 8 cm, taper both ends

Petiole 6 mm

Leaf margins waved. **Serration** remote

Leaves cupped, glossier and paler below. **Apex** often droops

Flowers 2.5 cm

Fruit to 1.5 cm, in 5-lobed calyx

Shoot slightly hairy, zig-zagged, speckled black

Pedicels 2–4 cm

Buds 4 mm, hairy, adpressed, conic, pale greenish-brown

A native of Japan and China, Snowbell tree grows to 10 m with a dense, rounded crown of horizontal branches. Storax (*S. officinalis*) is a smaller tree with white down on the young twigs, leaves and flowers. It has ovate, cordate leaves and round fruits.

Bigleaf storax

Styrax obassia

Leaves 10 cm, up to 15 cm on young trees

Flowers set unilaterally in racemes of 20–25

Flowers 2–3 cm

Fruit 1.5 cm, tomentose

Leaves densely pubescent and glaucous below. **Petiole** 2 cm, encloses bud

Native to Japan, Bigleaf storax has a grey bark and an open, upright crown that reaches 15 m. Hemsley storax (*S. hemsleyana*) carries its white flowers on short, pubescent racemes. The petioles of its less downy leaves do not enclose the bud.

Snowdrop tree

Halesia monticola

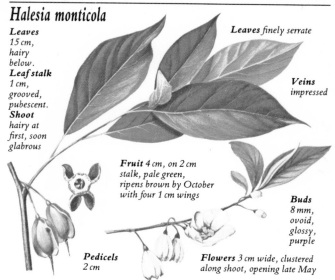

Leaves 15 cm, hairy below. **Leaf stalk** 1 cm, grooved, pubescent. **Shoot** hairy at first, soon glabrous

Leaves finely serrate

Veins impressed

Fruit 4 cm, on 2 cm stalk, pale green, ripens brown by October with four 1 cm wings

Buds 8 mm, ovoid, glossy, purple

Pedicels 2 cm

Flowers 3 cm wide, clustered along shoot, opening late May

Snowdrop tree is native to the mountains of the south-eastern USA and is distinguished by its fruit and flowers. Carolina snowdrop (*H. carolina*) is shrubbier with smaller flowers and fruit.

Loosestrife family Lythraceae

Crape myrtle

Lagerstroemia indica

Flowers 4 cm, in 20 cm panicles

Crown rounded dome

10 m. Crown dense. **Branches** slender. **Bark** silky grey, flaky, smooth; lighter underbark

Flowers terminate new shoots. **Petals** (6) crinkled, on long peduncle

Leaves 6 cm, entire, glabrous. **Shoot** angled

This native of China and Japan only produces its splendid flowers in climates with long, hot summers. The flowers are usually bright pink but can be white, purple or scarlet. The buds and leaves may be set in pairs, threes or singly along the same shoot.

Olive family Oleaceae

The main features of this family of about 400 trees and shrubs are the opposite, simple or pinnate leaves and the perfect or unisexual flowers with 2 stamens. The fruit may be a drupe, capsule or samara. Ash is the main tree genus and has fissured barks and shoots flattened between the buds. The fruit is a samara while *Olea*, *Ligustrum* and *Phillyrea* have simple leaves and a drupaceous fruit.

Ash

Fraxinus excelsior

♂ *flowers* have stamens set more densely than ♀s

Buds 6 mm

Flowers *without petals or sepals, open April, before leaves*

♀ *flowers* spreading

Branches *ascend*　　**Bole** *long*

45 m. Crown *light, open.* **Bark** *smooth when young, ridged, thick and grey in older trees*

Shoot *green-grey with white lenticels*

Leaves *30 cm, pale and white haired below.* **Rachis** *glabrous, grooved*

Terminal leaflet *on 2 cm petiole*

Leaflets *(9–13) 12 cm, toothed, fall while still green*

Fruit *4 cm, in pendulous bunches, ripening brown in October, persisting after leaves fall.* **Wing tips** *obtuse or notched*

Native throughout Europe and Asia Minor, Ash is a large forest tree that grows best on heavy, alkaline loams. While male and female flowers normally appear on separate trees, one tree may carry both sexes. The squat, black buds and smooth twigs are its best identification features. Red ash (*F. pennsylvanica*) has reddish buds, 7–9 leaflets and a brown, shallowly fissured bark.

Some cultivars of Ash

'Pendula': 10 m. Crown grafted at height of 3 m (or higher) to rootstock of Ash. **Branches** twist

'Jaspidea': Shoot yellow or golden by end of summer, flattened near bud. **Bud** 6 mm, black, true to type. **Leaflet** (below) yellow in spring, gold in autumn

'Diversifolia': Leaves (right) simple, occasionally trifoliate. **Petiole** 10 cm. **Veins** prominent below. **Bud** black

Serration very variable, usually coarse but sometimes very fine

'Pendula' or Weeping ash is readily identified by its habit, although one form reaching 30 m is less weeping and has some erect shoots. 'Jaspidea' is noted for its yellow shoots and foliage. The leaves and crown of 'Diversifolia' can confuse identification but the fruit, twigs and buds are identical to the type.

Manna ash

Fraxinus ornus

Leaflets (5–9) to 10 cm, stalked, downy below

Flowers in dense 15 cm panicles, fragrant, appear in May with leaves

Petals 5 mm, set in 4s, whitish yellow, narrow and linear

Teeth rounded

Petiolule 1.5 cm

Leaves 30 cm. **Rachis** bends, slender, grooved, pubescent at leaflet joints

Shoot almost glabrous, speckled with white lenticels

Manna ash reaches 20 m to form a tree similar to *F. excelsior*, but distinguished from it, when not in flower, by its stalked, pubescent leaflets and grey-brown, hairy buds. It grows wild in southern Europe and western Asia and is sometimes tapped for the sugary substance which exudes from the bark and gives the tree its common name.

Caucasian ash

Fraxinus oxycarpa

Leaflets cupped

Leaflets (7–9) 7 cm, shiny, pubescent on underside midrib vein

Leaflets sharply serrate

25 m. Crown narrow when young, later broadens

Bole straight.
Bark smooth, grey

Leaves 25 cm

Shoot glabrous, green or brown.
Buds set in 2s or 3s, coffee-coloured

This ash grows wild from southern Europe across the Caucasus to Iran and is usually encountered as the clone 'Raywood', whose leaves turn claret in autumn. Narrow-leafed ash (*F. angustifolia*) has slender, glabrous leaflets and a rougher, dark grey bark.

Velvet ash

Fraxinus velutina

Buds 5 mm, velvety, 6-scaled

Fruit 2 cm on downy pedicel. **Wing** shorter than seed, notched

Leaflets downy

Shoot round, slender, velvety in 1st year

Leaflets 5 cm, thick, bluntly toothed above middle, usually in 5s or, less often, 3s, 7s or 9s

Leaf 15 cm

Although some forms are almost glabrous, Velvet or Arizona ash, from the south-western USA and Mexico, has pubescence even on its flower panicles. It can stand great extremes of temperature and reaches 10 or 15 m. The bark is broadly ridged.

Olive

Olea europaea

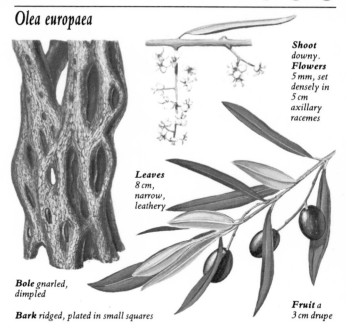

Shoot *downy.*
Flowers
*5 mm, set
densely in
5 cm
axillary
racemes*

Leaves
*8 cm,
narrow,
leathery*

Bole *gnarled,
dimpled*

Bark *ridged, plated in small squares*

Fruit *a
3 cm drupe*

A common feature of the Mediterranean landscape, the Olive has a densely branched crown that reaches 15 m as an orchard tree but when growing wild is much shrubbier and has small, oval leaves. If to be eaten, the fruit is usually harvested when green; for oil production it is generally left until black and fully ripe.

Tree privet

Ligistrum lucidum

Leaves *10 cm, entire,
folded along midrib, dark,
glossy above, paler and
matt below*

Flowers *creamy-white,
fragrant, in many 15 cm
conic panicles*

15 m. Crown *dense*

Petiole
1.5 cm

Shoot *slender*

Branches *radiate.*
Bark *smooth, grey.*
Fruit *2 mm, bloomed*

This superb Chinese evergreen is noted for its glossy and leathery leaves and the lateness of its flowers which open in autumn. Lilac (*Syringa vulgaris*) flowers in May and June and is deciduous with stout shoots ending in large pairs of green buds.

Phillyrea

Phillyrea latifolia

Leaves *6 cm, variable, opposite, with 7–12 pairs of lateral veins*

Fruit stalk *1 cm*

Surface *glossy above, matt beneath with prominent veins*

Fruit *1 cm, ripens red to blackish purple*

Midrib *raised*

Apex *acute.* **Buds** *minute*

Margins *toothed or entire.* **Shoot** *initially downy*

Phillyrea, found in evergreen woods in the Mediterranean region, reaches 10 m. It has a rounded crown with very glossy foliage which appears almost black, and a dense, shrub-like habit. The bark is smooth and grey. Its small, whitish green flowers appear in short axillary clusters during June.

Figwort family Scrophulariaceae

Paulownia

Paulownia tomentosa

Leaves *35 cm, texture very thin*

Margins *entire or with 4–6 teeth*

Flowers *5 cm in panicles to 30 cm, fragrant*

Shoot *stout with prominent lenticels, initially downy*

Petiole *15 cm, downy, pink-yellow*

Buds *minute*

Calyx *downy, pale brown, covers winter flower buds*

Flowers *bell-like*

A native of China, Paulownia, also called Foxglove tree, has a gaunt, domed crown and reaches 20 m. The flowers are often damaged over winter when fully exposed in bud. They are followed by green, ovoid, pointed capsules containing winged seeds.

Bignonia family Bignoniaceae

Indian bean tree ● Northern catalpa

Catalpa bignonioides ● *Catalpa speciosa*

Flowers 5 cm, open mid-July, in dense 20 cm conical or rounded conic panicles. *Corolla* campanulate, crinkled. *Calyx* glabrous

Petiole 15 cm, glabrous

Catalpa bignonioides leaf 25 cm, thin, abruptly acuminate

Fruit pod 40 cm, 7 mm wide, several from each flower panicle, purple-green, ripening brown October, persist through winter

C. speciosa leaf 25 cm, leathery

Shoot stout, smooth. *Leaf scars* prominent. *Bud* small, terminal lacking

Petiole 18 cm, hairy. *Buds* in 2s or 3s

The catalpas are a small group of trees with large ovate leaves and long, hanging pods. The commonest, Indian bean tree, from the gulf coast of America, forms a low, spreading tree, occasionally to 20 m. Northern catalpa, from central USA, has a conic crown and may attain 40 m, or half this height in Europe. Its flowers, to 6 cm, open earlier and the calyx is hairy. The chinese Yellow catalpa (*C. ovata*) has yellower 3 cm flowers and broadly ovate 3-lobed leaves with long tips. Hybrid catalpa (*C. x erubescens*) has leaves opening purple.

187

Agave family Agavaceae

Cabbage palm

Cordyline australis

Leaves *90 cm, lanceolate, pointed tip, erect, later drooping, persisting dead*

10 m

Bark *greyish, fissured into small, corky ridges*

Branches *erect, becoming spreading*

Crown *on large, straight bole*

Cabbage palm, from New Zealand, is hardy in coastal regions. Leaves are arranged spirally in tufts on shoots. The fragrant, creamy-white flowers are carried in terminal panicles up to 1 m high and are followed by numerous 6 mm bluish-white berries.

Palm family Palmaceae

Chusan palm

Trachycarpus fortunei

Top branches *radiate*

Bark *in cloth-like layers; peels in sheets*

Bark *very fibrous*

Leaves *open dark green*

10 m

Crown *on single bole.* **Leaves** *spread at top, drooping lower down*

Petiole *edges toothed*

Leaf *120 cm wide, in 40–60 folded segments*

Petiole *1 m*

Chusan palm, also called Windmill palm, from central China, is the palm most tolerant of cold and remarkable for its cloth-like bark. Like all true palms it has only a single growing point and so never branches.

188

Index

Entries refer to spp, vars and cvs described in detail and illustrated; for related trees see genus or nearest sp entry.

191